REVISE AQA GCSE

English and English Language

REVISION WORKBOOK

Foundation

Series Consultant: Harry Smith

Author: David Grant

THE REVISE AQA SERIES

Available in print or online

Online editions for all titles in the Revise AQA series are available Summer 2013.

Presented on our ActiveLearn platform, you can view the full book and customise it by adding notes, comments and weblinks.

Print editions

English and English Language Revision Workbook Foundation
9781447940685

English and English Language Revision Guide Foundation
9781447940647

Online editions

English and English Language Revision Workbook Foundation
9781447940760

English and English Language Revision Guide Foundation
9781447940722

This Revision Workbook is designed to complement your classroom and home learning, and to help prepare you for the exam. It does not include all the content and skills needed for the complete course. It is designed to work in combination with Pearson's main AQA GCSE English 2010 Series.

To find out more visit:
www.pearsonschools.co.uk/aqagcseenglishrevision

Contents

1-to-1 page match with the Revision Guide ISBN 9781447940647

A small bit of small print
AQA publishes Sample Assessment Material and the Specification on its website. This is the official content and this book should be used in conjunction with it. The questions in this book have been written to help you practise what you have learned in your revision. Remember: the real exam questions may not look like this.

Questions 1 and 2

The exam paper is split into two sections:

- Section A: Reading
- Section B: Writing

In the Reading section of your exam paper, you will be asked **four** different kinds of question. Each question will ask you to complete one of these types of task:

1 **(a)** Locate and list relevant information from a source text.

(b) Locate and show understanding of relevant information from a source text.

2 Understand and infer relevant information from a source text and explain it.

3 Comment on the use of language in a source text and its effect on the reader.

4 Compare the use of presentation and its effect in two source texts.

Each exam question is intended to assess you on one or both of the assessment objectives:

a *Read and understand texts, selecting material appropriate to purpose.*

b *Explain and evaluate how writers use linguistic, grammatical, structural and presentational features to achieve effects and engage and influence the reader, supporting your comments with detailed textual references.*

Don't try to answer the exam-style questions on this page – just get used to the style.

1 **(a)** Look at the exam-style questions below. For each question, identify the type of task you are being asked to complete and circle either one or both of the assessment objectives on which each question is assessing you.

> **1** **(a)** Read **Source 1**. List four things you learn about the city of Birmingham. *(4 marks)*

Task: 1a 1b 2 3 4 AOs: **a** **b**

(b)

> **(b)** What do you learn from **Source 1** about the people of Birmingham and their hopes for the future? *(4 marks)*

Task: 1a 1b 2 3 4 AOs: **a** **b**

(c)

> **2** What reasons are given in **Source 2** to persuade the reader to donate money to this cause?
> Remember to:
> - show your understanding by explaining in your own words
> - support your ideas using the text. *(8 marks)*

Task: 1a 1b 2 3 4 AOs: **a** **b**

Had a go ☐ Nearly there ☐ Nailed it! ☐

Questions 3 and 4

In the Reading section of your exam paper, you will be asked **four** different kinds of question. Each question will ask you to complete one of these types of task:

1 **(a)** Locate and list relevant information from a source text.

(b) Locate and show understanding of relevant information from a source text.

2 Understand and infer relevant information from a source text and explain it.

3 Comment on the use of language in a source text and its effect on the reader.

4 Compare the use of presentation and its effect in two source texts.

Each exam question is intended to assess you on one or both of the assessment objectives:

a *Read and understand texts, selecting material appropriate to purpose.*

b *Explain and evaluate how writers use linguistic, grammatical, structural and presentational features to achieve effects and engage and influence the reader, supporting your comments with detailed textual references.*

Don't try to answer the exam-style questions on this page – just get used to the style.

1 Look at the exam-style questions below. For each question, identify the type of task you are being asked to complete and circle either one or both of the assessment objectives on which each question is assessing you.

(a)

> **3** How does the writer use **language features** in **Source 3**?
> Remember to:
> - give some examples of language features
> - explain the effects.
>
> *(12 marks)*

Task: 1a 1b 2 3 4 AOs: **a** **b**

(b)

> **4** Now you need to refer to **Source 3**, and either **Source 1** or **Source 2**. Compare the way that both texts use **presentational features** for effect.
> Remember to:
> - write about the way the **sources** are **presented**
> - explain the **effect** of the presentational features
> - compare the way they **look**.
>
> *(12 marks)*

Task: 1a 1b 2 3 4 AOs: **a** **b**

Planning your time in the exam

Look at the examples of the kinds of questions you can expect to find in the Reading section of your exam. On the exam paper, you are advised to spend **one hour** on **Section A: Reading** and **one hour** on **Section B: Writing**.

Time allowed
2 hours and 15 minutes

1 **(a)** Read **Source 1**. List four things you learn about the city of Birmingham. *(4 marks)*

(b) What do you learn from **Source 1** about the people of Birmingham and their hopes for the future? *(4 marks)*

2 What reasons are given in **Source 2** to persuade the reader to donate money to this cause? *(8 marks)*

3 How does the writer use **language features** in **Source 3**? *(12 marks)*

4 Now you need to refer to **Source 3**, and either **Source 1** or **Source 2**. Compare the way that both texts use **presentational features** for effect. *(12 marks)*

1. How minutes should you spend reading the source texts and the questions to familiarise yourself with them?
   Answer: .... minutes
2. How many minutes should you spend writing your answer to Question 1a?
   Answer: .... minutes
3. How many minutes should you spend writing your answer to Question 1b?
   Answer: .... minutes
4. How many minutes should you spend writing your answer to Question 2?
   Answer: .... minutes
5. How many minutes should you spend writing your answer to Question 3?
   Answer: .... minutes
6. How many minutes should you spend writing your answer to Question 4?
   Answer: .... minutes
7. Which of the following should you do before you start to answer any of the questions? Circle your choices.

Jot down a quick plan of your ideas for each question.	Read the source texts.	Read the questions.	Highlight relevant information to help you answer questions.	Read the source texts a second time.

Reading the questions

Look at the exam-style question below:

> **2** What reasons are given in **Source 2** to persuade the reader to donate money to this cause? *(8 marks)*

1 Identify:

(a) which source texts you are being asked to write about ....

(b) the keywords in the question which tell you what to do ....

(c) the number of marks for this question ....

(d) how long you should spend writing your answer to this question ....

2 Look at the exam-style questions below. For each question, identify:

- the source text
- the keywords that tell you what to do
- the number of marks available
- how long you should spend on each question.

> **1 (b)** What do you learn from **Source 1** about the people of Birmingham and their hopes for the future? *(4 marks)*

....

> **3** How does the writer use **language features** in **Source 3**? *(12 marks)*

....

> **4** Now you need to refer to **Source 3**, and either **Source 1** or **Source 2**. Compare the way that both texts use **presentational features** for effect. *(12 marks)*

....

Approaching the exam paper

Before you go into the exam, be sure how you will spend the first 15 minutes of the exam.

Before you start answering the questions, you should be sure you know what they are asking you to do. So look closely at each question in order to:

- identify the source text it is asking you about
- identify the keywords in the question which tell you what to do
- identify the keywords in the question which tell you the feature or features you should write about
- plan how long you will spend answering the question.

Look at the exam-style questions below and then complete activities 1 and 2.

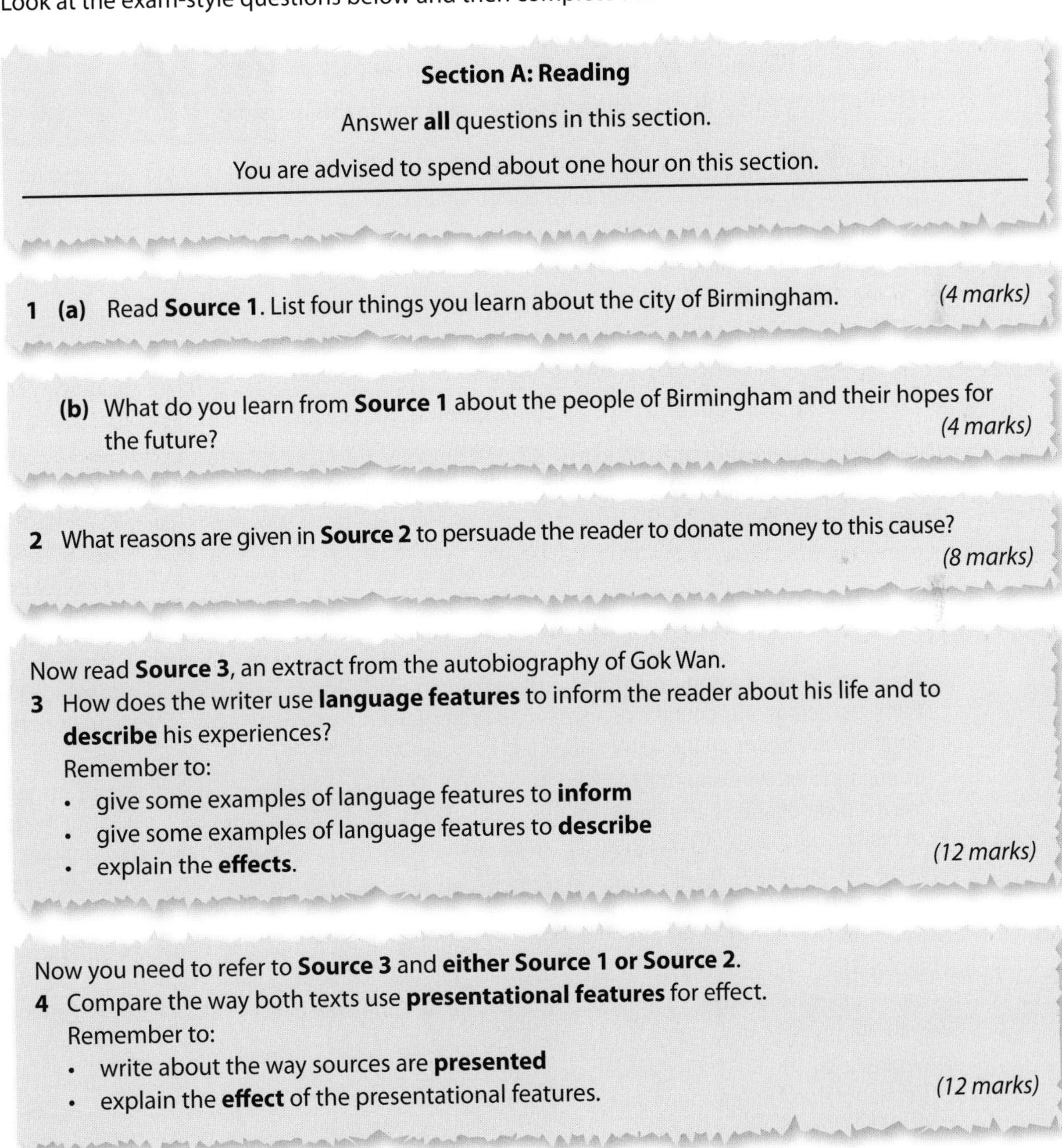

Section A: Reading

Answer **all** questions in this section.

You are advised to spend about one hour on this section.

1 (a) Read **Source 1**. List four things you learn about the city of Birmingham. *(4 marks)*

(b) What do you learn from **Source 1** about the people of Birmingham and their hopes for the future? *(4 marks)*

2 What reasons are given in **Source 2** to persuade the reader to donate money to this cause? *(8 marks)*

Now read **Source 3**, an extract from the autobiography of Gok Wan.

3 How does the writer use **language features** to inform the reader about his life and to **describe** his experiences?

Remember to:

- give some examples of language features to **inform**
- give some examples of language features to **describe**
- explain the **effects**. *(12 marks)*

Now you need to refer to **Source 3** and **either Source 1 or Source 2**.

4 Compare the way both texts use **presentational features** for effect.

Remember to:

- write about the way sources are **presented**
- explain the **effect** of the presentational features. *(12 marks)*

1 Circle the key information in all five questions.

2 Use the space below to plan out the hour that you should allow for **Section A: Reading**.

Skimming for the main idea

Look at the headline and opening sentence of the online newspaper article below (**Source 1**), then answer Question 1.

Source 1

Clean the bones of your relatives and party in their graveyards: Welcome to the Day of the Dead

Though at first glance these people seem to have taken Halloween a bit too far, they are in fact taking part in a yearly ritual in which they celebrate their dead relatives.

The Day of the Dead is observed across Mexico and also in other places including Haiti, Colombia, Guatemala, El Salvador and the United States.

1 What do the headline and the opening sentence suggest the article will be about?

....

....

Now look at the rest of the article for just 20 seconds, then answer Question 2.

> Skim reading a text can give you a good idea of what it is about before you read it more closely. Look at the headline or title, the first sentence of each paragraph and the last sentence of the text to help you get the main idea of the text.

Mexicans clean the bones of their dead and decorate their graves with flowers and candy skulls. Families across the country bring picnics to cemeteries, decorate graves with marigolds and sprinkle holy water on the tombs of their loved ones.

Thousands of Peruvians crowd Lima's Virgen de Lourdes cemetery, the country's largest, to leave flower offerings and dance to music. Hilarion Ramos, 79, left a bouquet of lilies at the grave of his son who died in 1979 at age 2. 'My little boy left 33 years ago, but I don't forget him. I still have the memory of his little face in my mind,' said Ramos, who walked a mile to take his offering to the cemetery.

Food plays a big role in Bolivia where many people celebrate the 'return' of loved ones with full tables. Fruit, bread and wine were set on a white tablecloth for Blanca Jimenez's dead family members, who were represented by framed photographs next to lit candles. 'It's a re-encounter with our loved ones,' Jimenez explained.

'Today is the day we come to celebrate the people who have died, the people we haven't seen in a long time,' priest Jean-Robert Pierre said. 'We're celebrating our ancestors.'

2 Sum up the newspaper article in one sentence.

....

....

....

Annotating the sources

Read the opening paragraph of the newspaper article below (**Source 1**), then answer Question 1.

Source 1

Bradley Wiggins: please don't ask my wife to take a picture

As Britain's first Tour de France winner and arguably the country's most celebrated current athlete, Bradley Wiggins is now recognised wherever he goes. But he says that while he appreciates the warm public reaction, such a level of fame brings difficulties – particularly for his family.

1 Which details from **Source 1** would help you to answer the exam-style question below? Tick the ones that are relevant to the question.

1 **(b)** What are Bradley Wiggins' feelings about fame? *(4 marks)*

A Britain's first Tour de France winner

B Bradley Wiggins is now recognised wherever he goes

C he appreciates the warm public reaction

D fame brings difficulties

E particularly for his family

Now look at the rest of the newspaper article, then answer Question 2.

'They ask your wife to take the photo, which is a bit rude,' Wiggins says of some well-wishers. 'And after a while that becomes tiresome, especially when you're having a pizza with your children, or you have to have a photo with somebody else's kids while yours stand to the side.'

Wiggins, 32, says he finds it particularly hard that his celebrity takes any attention from his wife, who is herself a British champion. He says: 'Nobody ever asks her how she is. It's always, "How's Brad doing?" Nobody ever says to her, "How are you doing, Cath? How are you handling it all?" It's very difficult for her.'

Earlier in his career, in a lull following his three-medal haul from the 2004 Olympics, Wiggins had a period in which he drank heavily. In the interview he describes a period when he would arrive at his local pub when it opened, often staying to drink 12 pints of beer. 'I was just bored and didn't know what to do.' The nine-month binge caused the usually beanpole-framed cyclist to put on significant weight: 'I got quite big. I wasn't huge. I was probably 83 kilos.'

It ended when his son, Ben, was born: 'We had a baby. So then it was a case of, well, I've got to earn some money and the responsibility takes over.'

A lack of money had been one of the post-Olympic depressions Wiggins faced. He says: 'It got me down. You think if you win the Olympics, you'll become a millionaire overnight. But I was still scraping the barrel, looking down the back of the settee for pound coins to buy a pint of milk.'

2 Highlight any details from the rest of the newspaper article that would help you answer the exam-style question above.

Had a go ☐ Nearly there ☐ Nailed it! ☐

Selecting information

Read the opening paragraph of the newspaper article below (**Source 1**), then answer Question 1.

Source 1

The Skeleton Coast from above

It takes three attempts to shut the cockpit door, and we rock the tiny aircraft in the process. The pilot and trainee, three passengers and too many bags, are all sardined into a tin box on a dusty airstrip, the distant mountains diminished by haze.

1 Which details would help you to answer the exam-style question below? Tick the ones that are relevant to the question.

1 (a) List **four** things we learn about where the writer has been and what he has been doing from the article? *(4 marks)*

A It takes three attempts to shut the cockpit door

B tiny aircraft

C The pilot and trainee, three passengers and too many bags

D sardined into a tin box

E distant mountains

Now look at the rest of the newspaper article, then answer Question 2.

'Clear prop!' The engine splutters into life. Soon we are cantering along, gathering speed and generously throwing up dust for all and sundry. But there is no all, and there is no sundry, just our guide sitting nonchalantly astride the bonnet of his 4×4 to wave off another batch of wilderness seekers. Some distance behind him, two fire buckets hang, lifeless, from a T-shaped frame next to the lavatory, which has a pointed roof made from sticks. That's it. There is no control tower, no emergency services – just miles and miles of nothingness.

We are heading to our camp, a comfortable oasis of calm beside the river. By air it is a relatively straightforward journey; back in the 4×4, it would involve a huge amount of bumping, churning and sliding over desert rock and sand to get there.

The altimeter needle continues to turn as the views widen; detail is lost as patterns emerge, nature's patterns, completely devoid of influence from man's busying hand. At cruising height, the desert gives way to mountains, carved and fissured rock massifs.

Dry rivers trace steep-sided valleys, where twin lines of hardy bushes mark the boundaries of an infrequent flow of water. But within this seeming barrenness is life.

We have witnessed the regal oryx with his lethal horns, striding the plains and scampering up mountain slopes; the desert-adapted rhino with his grumpy ways, his lumbering, trundling gait. The list goes on; life goes on, resilient, changing.

Then the pilot smiles and offers us a spherical bag. 'We're landing soon to refuel – anyone for biltong?'

2 Highlight any information from the rest of the article that would help you answer the exam-style question above.

Purpose and audience

Look at the different texts below. For each one, identify the writer's intended audience and purpose. For each of your answers, write a sentence explaining your decision.

The first things you should think about when you have read a text are its purpose and its audience. Note, though, you won't be asked **directly** in the exam to identify a text's purpose and audience.

Guided

1

Kanye Omari West was born in 1977. His father was a former activist and photographer, his mother a university English professor. With four Number 1 albums under his belt, West diversified, launching a fashion range and a chain of fast food restaurants, all of which have contributed to the huge amount of money donated to his charitable foundation supporting African American children's education.

The audience for this text is teenagers and younger adults because I think they would be interested in Kanye West, although the formal language makes it appropriate for all adults. The purpose of the text is to ....

....

....

....

2

Eating a healthy dinner at school could make the biggest difference to your education. It can help your concentration and, when you're concentrating, you learn more. It's not just about how much you eat – it's what you eat that really matters. And don't think it's just 'lay off the chips and chocolate'. You need fruit and vegetables as well – five portions of them everyday.

....

....

....

....

3

Sitting in our cabin, staring out at the snow, we witnessed one of the most extraordinary sights of our lives. As we watched, a herd of reindeer approached. The first thing that strikes you about them is their size. They're enormous. And despite their huge heads and ungainly antlers, they are astonishingly beautiful. Even the bald one with huge clumps of matted fur dangling from its backside like Christmas decorations.

....

....

....

....

Putting it into practice

Read **Source 1** below, then have a go at the exam-style question opposite.

Source 1

THE MESSIEST OBSTACLE COURSE IN THE WORLD

Thousands of the hardiest – and possibly craziest – competitors in the country have just completed one of the most gruelling obstacle courses in the world.

The Tough Mudder Extreme Endurance Challenge was designed by British Special Forces to be one of the most extreme tests of all-round strength, stamina, mental grit and camaraderie. And the 2012 edition held in the grounds of Drumlanrig Castle and Country Estate in Dumfriesshire, lived up to its billing.

The near 9,000 people who took to the start line to take part in the 'endurance phenomenon' and 'ultimate test of team work' had to overcome up to 30 different obstacles – including electric wires designed to shock participants and a mile-long muddy ditch.

Contestants paid up to £90 to take on the course. Each participant takes on average almost four hours to complete the course. The course is so tough, one in five are expected to drop out before ever seeing the finish line.

The series of extreme endurance events began in 2009 in the USA but since then have taken off on this side of the Atlantic. So far, more than half a million people worldwide have pitted themselves against the course.

Putting in into practice

1 (a) List **four** things which you learn about the Tough Mudder Extreme Endurance Challenge. *(4 marks)*

When you tackle this kind of question in the exam, remember to:

- spend around 6 minutes answering it
- read the source text carefully, highlighting any information about the Challenge
- select points that are relevant to the question
- avoid copying out chunks of text.

Remember: You will have more space than this to answer the question in the exam. Use your own paper to finish your answer to the question above.

Had a go ☐ Nearly there ☐ Nailed it! ☐

The writer's viewpoint

Read the headline and the opening of the newspaper article below (**Source 1**), then answer Question 1.

Source 1

We have become a nation of cry-babies!

Ah, such wonderful news that Europe won the Ryder Cup! We beat America, we trounced the Yankee's doodle dandy, we snatched victory from almost certain defeat, making this golf tournament the final magnificent huzzah in a long summer of sporting glory which ... hang on a minute. Why are all these men in blue plaid jackets and neat slacks standing around, crying fit to burst? Why are they weeping like bridesmaids who've just had their bouquets nicked? Buck up, Ryder team.

1 Write one or two sentences summing up the writer's viewpoint.

....

....

....

....

....

....

....

Now read more of the article, then answer Questions 2 and 3.

There is a worrying side to all this. Yes, crying can be good for emotional health, but what happens when the rough stuff of life hits you square in the jaw?

Your prospects of coping with a genuine dilemma or emergency are slim to nil.

Surely there is a need to conserve emotions; to store tears for the times that really matter, for the great trials of life that lie ahead, as surely they must.

Far too many people cry for no other reason than they are feeling sorry for themselves.

Get a grip. On your hankie, if nothing else.

2 Do you still think your answer to Question 1 effectively sums up the writer's viewpoint? If not, write another sentence or two, summing up their viewpoint.

....

....

....

....

3 Write down three short quotations from the article that helped you to answer Questions 1 and 2, then write one or two sentences explaining how each one helped you to work out the writer's viewpoint.

(a) ....

....

....

(b) ....

....

....

(c) ....

....

....

A short quotation could even be a one-word quotation. Sometimes the writer's language choice can tell you a lot about their viewpoint.

Fact, opinion and expert evidence

Look at the three extracts from online articles below, then answer Question 1.

A **Last year, more than 800 businesses failed each and every day.**

B Professor Trevor Carter's research strongly suggests that poverty is the root cause.

C **There is nothing more delicious than warm, fresh bread.**

1 Identify which of these extracts is:

(a) a fact ....   **(b)** an opinion ....   **(c)** expert evidence ....

Now read the newspaper article (**Source 1**) below, and answer Questions 2 and 3.

Source 1

How GM crops have increased the use of danger pesticides and created superweeds and toxin-resistant insects

Planting GM crops has led to an increase rather than a decrease in the use of pesticides in the last 16 years, according to US scientists. The researchers said that the plants have caused superweeds and toxin-resistant insects to emerge, meaning farmers not only have to use more pesticides on their crops overall, but also are using older and more dangerous chemicals. The team at Washington State University found the weight of chemicals used on US farms has increased by 183 million kilos since GM crops were introduced in 1996.

The findings dramatically undermine the case for adopting the crops, which were sold to farmers and shoppers on the basis that they would reduce the need to be treated with powerful chemicals. However, the reality is that a number of weeds have developed immunity to the chemical and are now able to swamp farmers' fields. The overall effect is that desperate farmers are now using a cocktail of many different chemicals to try to tame the weeds.

Study leader Professor Charles Benbrook said: 'Resistant weeds have become a major problem for many farmers reliant on GM crops and are now driving up the volume of herbicide needed each year by about 25 per cent.'

2 Write one sentence summing up the writer's viewpoint in the article.

....

....

3 Identify at least one fact, one opinion and one piece of expert evidence the writer has used to support his viewpoint, then write a sentence explaining how it does this.

Fact: ....

....

Opinion: ....

....

Expert evidence: ....

....

Had a go ☐ Nearly there ☐ Nailed it! ☐

Inference

Read the opening of a newspaper article about foxes, then answer Questions 1 and 2.

> They are as big as Alsatians and getting bigger. Their numbers are increasing and are out of control. They foul our gardens, they rip cats apart. It is simply a matter of time before they kill a baby.

1 Write down two words or phrases from the article which suggest we should be worried about foxes.

(a) ....

(b) ....

Guided **2** What impression of foxes does the article give you?

The article makes me think that foxes ....

....

Now read the rest of the article, then complete the question that follows. Remember to use at least one short quotation from the text to support your answer.

> It's incredible how much hysteria the British press can generate about such a small, and largely inoffensive, animal as the fox.
>
> In the war on the urban fox, truth is irrelevant. The fox 'cub' recently pictured sitting on a child's bed in London was actually an adult in the terminal stages of mange. It had crept into the house to try to keep warm (foxes with mange lose most of their fur): it caused no problem and was removed by the RSPCA. A non-story and an everyday occurrence with stray cats.
>
> The first claim that foxes will kill a baby appeared in the *Sunday Times* in 1973: 40 years on, this still has not happened. In comparison, the seven children and five adults killed by dogs since 2005, and the hundreds more disfigured, receive far less coverage.

Guided **1 (b)** What are the writer's feelings about urban foxes? *(4 marks)*

Use inference to work out the writer's attitude – and remember to read the whole extract carefully before you decide what the writer's attitude is.

The writer begins the article by making foxes sound aggressive and dangerous. He describes the fox population as 'out of control' and describes how they can 'rip cats apart'. This is a shocking picture of foxes.

As the article goes on the writer says that this shocking picture is not the truth, it is just the way that newspapers describe urban foxes. For example, the writer explains that

....

....

....

....

....

Point-Evidence-Explain

Read the newspaper article below (**Source 1**), then answer the questions that follow.

Source 1

Coping with the first day at school

For some youngsters, walking through those school gates in their uniform for the first time provokes great excitement. Others find it thoroughly nerve-wracking as they enter the great unknown.

Every child is different – and as the mother of three daughters I should know. My eldest girl couldn't have been more thrilled about the prospect of sitting in a classroom and we counted down the days for weeks beforehand. In the event she thought it was all a huge let-down and ended her first day adamant that it would be her last. When we explained that she had many years of schooling ahead of her she was livid.

An effective way to support your answers to questions that ask you to explain or compare is to use Point-Evidence-Explain paragraphs.

An effective way to support your answers to questions that ask you to explain or compare is to use Point-Evidence-Explain paragraphs.

1 The point below could be used to comment on the writer's use of language and its effect. Which piece of evidence from **Source 1** most effectively supports it?

Point: The writer describes how excited her eldest daughter was about going to school.

Evidence A: 'thrilled'

Evidence B: 'we counted down the days'

Evidence C: 'every child is different'

To develop your point and evidence, you need to explain how they answer the question.

....

....

2 Which of these explanations most effectively develops the point and the supporting evidence?

Point: The writer describes how excited her eldest daughter was about going to school.

Evidence: For example, she says her daughter was 'thrilled' and that 'we counted down the days'.

Explain A: These quotes show how excited her daughter was.

Explain B: The word 'thrilled' emphasises just how excited she was, making school sound like an adventure.

Explain C: Counting down the days is something a lot of children do at Christmas time using an advent calendar.

3 Write one or two sentences, explaining which explanation you think is more effective and why.

....

....

Had a go ☐ Nearly there ☐ Nailed it! ☐

Putting it into practice

Read **Source 1** below, then have a go at the exam-style question opposite.

Source 1

Sir Ranulph Fiennes: it's the winning that is important

At the age of 68, most men are collecting their bus pass. But not 'the world's greatest explorer', who is shuffling around a large warehouse near Bedford, desperately searching for his mobile telephone.

Sir Ranulph Fiennes – the only man to circumnavigate the globe on foot, traversing through both poles; conquer Everest, after suffering a heart attack on a previous attempt; climb the north face of the Eiger, despite suffering vertigo so badly that it is his wife who has to clean the gutters at home; and run seven marathons in seven days on seven continents for good measure – is on another mission.

First, though, he needs to find his phone amid the morass of polar equipment laid out on the floor. Having located it, he mutters and peers suspiciously at the screen before an aide explains that he has 43 voicemail messages. Ran, as he likes to be called, looks at me: 'I have no idea how this thing works.' I'm worried that his latest expedition might be a step too far if mastering a simple old Nokia is beyond him.

In December, as part of a six-man team, he will set off to cross the bleak wasteland of Antarctica – a task that has been achieved before, but never in the depths of midwinter, when the temperature averages –70C and occasionally plummets to –90C. The expedition has been nicknamed 'The Coldest Journey'.

I have joined him at an engineering centre in Bedford to see how the equipment fares at ultra low temperatures. In the warehouse is a glorified walk-in freezer. The electronic gauge on the outside wall reads –58.7C. I am given a pair of salopettes, boots and an ultra-thick down jacket.

At first, my body feels toasty warm, and apart from my nostrils icing up, I am fairly comfortable. Except for my hands. After five minutes, they go from a little cold to 'Um, actually, Ran, my fingers are in quite a bit of pain.'

He ignores me. I am not sure whether this is because his hearing is starting to go – he often cocks his head and says 'Eh?' – or because he thinks I am a wimp. Here, after all, is a man who has such a disregard for pain that he hacked off his own frostbitten fingers. He did this not in last-resort desperation on an expedition, but calmly in his garden shed because he did not fancy the idea of waiting five months for an operation. 'My wife said I was becoming very irritable every time I knocked them, so I bought a micro sword in the village shop.' He clamped his hand in a Black & Decker vice and proceeded to hack away. For five whole days. 'It didn't hurt at all. The surgeon at the hospital said I had done a very good job.' The top third of all of the fingers and thumb on his left hand are now stumps.

After 11 minutes in the cold chamber, I panic amid visions of my frozen hand requiring the Black & Decker treatment. 'I really need to leave now, I'm sorry,' I say in as forceful a way as possible for someone feeling very sheepish.

Putting it into practice

1 (b) What do you learn about Ranulph Fiennes that is interesting or surprising? *(4 marks)*

When you tackle this kind of question in the exam, remember to:

- spend around 6 minutes answering it
- read the source text carefully (for this question, highlighting any information about Ranulph Fiennes)
- select key points that are relevant to the question
- avoid copying out chunks of text.

Remember: You will have more space than this to answer the question in the exam. Use your own paper to finish your answer to the question above.

Had a go ☐ Nearly there ☐ Nailed it! ☐

Selecting evidence

Victoria Pendleton is an Olympic gold medal winning cyclist. Read **Source 1**, which is a short extract from her autobiography entitled *Between the Lines*, then answer Questions 1 and 2.

> Dad rode away from me as we climbed the hill on a cold and drizzly Sunday morning in Bedfordshire. 'He doesn't love me,' I said to myself as I tried to keep up with the distant figure of my father. 'He doesn't love me. He doesn't love me …'
>
> I repeated the words over and over again as, never lifting my gaze from the unbreakable man on the bike climbing the steep hill, I turned my legs as fast as I could. I had to hang onto Dad. I was sure that if I lost sight of him I would lose hold of his love.

1 Which of the quotes below would you use in an answer to this question:

> **1 (b)** How did Victoria Pendleton feel when she was training with her father? *(4 marks)*

A cold and drizzly Sunday morning

B He doesn't love me. He doesn't love me …'

C unbreakable

D the distant figure of my father

E if I lost sight of him I would lose hold of his love.

2 Which of the quotations above would allow you to comment on the writer's choice of language? Write one or two sentences about your chosen quotation, commenting on what it suggests about Victoria Pendleton's feelings when she was training with her father.

> Aim to choose quotations that:
> - allow you to focus on answering the question
> - contain a word, phrase or sentence structure that you think the writer has used for effect.

Quote: ....

....

....

Now read the next paragraphs from Pendleton's autobiography, then answer Question 3.

> I was fifteen. I had grown used to the ritual of chasing my father as he sped ahead of me. Dad dealt in clear and simple truths. He never told you that you were better than you were – even to boost you at your most vulnerable. Dad just expected you to do your best every single day. He was tough but, when I pleased him, I felt radiant with happiness. I knew how much it meant when Dad said he was proud of me.
>
> The rain trickled down my face. It might have looked like I was crying, but I wasn't. I was just concentrating and pedalling, pedalling and concentrating. But I was so tired and freezing I would no longer feel my hands on the handlebars or my feet on the pedals. I held on, numb to the finger-tips, pushing down with my churning legs and deadened feet. The gap between us might have widened but I would not let myself lose Dad. I clung onto the blurry image of him up ahead. An invisible twine must have bound his bike to mine.

3 Underline at least two more quotations that you could include in an answer to the exam-style question above.

Embedding quotations

In 2012, Felix Baumgartner completed his space jump, freefalling from a platform 24 miles above the earth. Read an extract from a newspaper interview with him below (**Source 1**), then answer Question 1.

Source 1

The man who fell to earth

Once he had left his capsule, Baumgartner began to whirl through space at a speed which sent him into a spin. 'I had one minute to find a solution. While spinning, I'm thinking: "Should I push the button to release my chute, to stop that spin? But that would mean it's over and I'm not going to fly supersonic – so should I tough it out and find a solution?"

'I had to maintain my cool and this is what I've been doing the last 25 years – being focused and not freaking out. In my head I was cool-minded. My worst fear was not dying, but failing to fly supersonic. I felt I had it under control.'

Guided

1 Using the short quotations shown in **A–D**, explain how Baumgartner felt as he fell towards earth.

A 'whirl' **B** 'tough it out' **C** 'maintain my cool' **D** 'freaking out'

As Baumgartner falls through space in a 'whirl', he starts to spin. He realises he must

....

....

Now read more of the article, then answer Question 2.

Baumgartner thinks hard when asked about his jump's sweetest moment. 'I had a couple of good moments,' he eventually says. 'One was standing with my feet outside the capsule just before I stepped off. We'd been working towards that for five years. As soon as I was standing there – completely released from all the cables – I knew it was going to happen. That was a big relief and a really unique, outstanding moment.

'And then when you open your parachute you know it's over – I'm still alive! Mike Todd was the last person I saw before going up. He'd said, "OK, see you on the ground, buddy." But you could tell he wasn't 100 per cent sure. I wasn't either. We prepare for the worst but hope for the best.'

2 Write one sentence explaining what you learn from the extract about Baumgartner's feelings during his space jump.

....

....

3 Circle four or five short quotations that you could use to support your answer to Question 2.

4 Rewrite your answer to Question 2 embedding at least two of the quotations you have circled.

....

....

....

Remember: Shorter quotations are often more effective than longer ones.
- They show the examiner that you can identify key words and phrases in the text.
- They allow you to focus on the writer's specific language choices.
- You don't waste time and ink copying out large chunks of the source text.

Had a go ☐ Nearly there ☐ Nailed it! ☐

Develop your explanations

Read the opening of the newspaper article below (**Source 1**).

Source 1

I was crushed by a cow

I look after about 300 cows on a farm in Gloucestershire and have built up a natural affinity with them – but I still remain wary. Three years ago, I was moving the Friesian herd out of a field and one rather lame cow crept up silently behind me. I waved my hands at her and shouted, 'Get back!' I wasn't concerned, just slightly irritated that she'd followed me. But as I turned to walk back to the yard, a force like the bonnet of a fast-moving car exploded in my back, throwing me facedown on the concrete track. It's not unusual for a cow to follow someone, but I'd never had a solitary beast charge at me like that.

Look at some extracts from one student's comments on the writer's feelings, then complete Question 1.

A The writer knows a lot about cows because he says he looks after 'about 300' of them.

B The writer describes the cow hitting him as a 'force' which he compares to a 'fast-moving car' that 'exploded in my back.'

C The word 'exploded' suggests the impact of the cow was extremely sudden, shocking and violent.

D After the incident, the writer describes the cow as a 'beast', which reinforces the impression that it is an unpredictable and dangerous animal. This contrasts sharply with the initial description of the cow as 'rather lame' and the fact that writer 'wasn't concerned', making the incident all the more shocking and violent.

E The writer says he was thrown 'facedown on the concrete track', which must have been painful.

1 Circle any relevant and effective comments on the writer's feelings above.

2 What would be the best order for your chosen comments? List them in order.

....

3 Now read another short extract from the article. Write one or two relevant and effective comments on the writer's feelings.

Shocked and winded, I rolled over and tried to get up, but the cow lowered her head and pushed it into my chest and stomach, crushing me into the ground. I felt the back legs of the 1,000lb beast folding, and realised she was going to sit on me.

It's hard to comprehend just how big a cow is until you're underneath one, looking up at it. I've no idea what made her so angry – I've waved at cows before and they've always backed off. But this one seemed possessed.

....

....

Word classes

Read the opening of the newspaper article below (**Source 1**), then answer Questions 1 and 2.

Source 1

At a loss in the Rocky Mountains

I lose handbags; I leave them behind when travelling – Italy (on a train), Norway (in a mountain cabin), Scotland (in a distillery). I had a safe canvas bag with a shoulder strap for Canada.

We headed along Highway One, the Trans-Canada Highway, a straight line far into the distance.

'You'd think the Romans had been here,' my husband said.

Not the Romans but the early pioneers, enterprising adventurers going west, not knowing what lay ahead. We knew. We were going to the Rocky Mountains. The land was flat as we left Calgary, the sprawling development making it difficult to know exactly when we did leave. Then we saw the profiles of the ski jumps, challenging monsters for other brave men, a legacy from the Winter Olympic Games in 1988. We stopped to take photographs and decided to have lunch in a local café.

1 Circle and label at least one noun, one verb, one adjective and one adverb in the extract.

2 In the opening sentence, the writer has used lots of **proper nouns:** Italy, Norway, Scotland.

What effect does this list of proper nouns create?

....

....

....

Read on, then answer Questions 3 and 4.

Then on again, the road developing ups and downs as the hills became mountains. We drove slowly, taking in the ever more spectacular view. At times it felt that we were diving down into a bowl surrounded by peaks. Just scribbles of cloud in the blue sky, the mountain tops clear, inviting photos that would never do justice to the landscape. When we reached Canmore, a ski resort near Banff, we decided to stop for a look around and to imagine the place in winter.

I opened the car door and reached down by my feet for my handbag. Not there. Nor on the back seat. I stood immobile as I relived the last hour or so of my life. The picture was as clear as that of the ski jumps. It was on the floor by my chair in the café.

3 Choose **one verb** from the extract above that you think is particularly effective. Write a sentence explaining the effect this verb has on the reader.

....

....

4 Find one or two sentences in the extract in which the writer has used lots of adjectives. What effect do they create?

....

....

....

....

....

....

Putting it into practice

Read the newspaper article below (**Source 1**), then have a go at the exam-style question opposite.

Source 1

Big in Belgium

Taylor Jones, 19, is a rapper who lives in London and has recently found fame in Belgium

It was late last summer, just after I stepped off the stage at Bobbejaanland, that it really hit me. I went for a walk around after the show… and I was being mobbed by fans – so much so that the organisers gave me security. It seemed surreal, especially because a few days earlier I'd been in London, where nobody gives you a second glance.

But this isn't something that I fell into – I've always dreamed of it. I sat in my bedroom in Swindon, where I grew up, singing, practising, working hard to make it happen. The rapping part was an accident. I had a bad cold one day and couldn't hit the notes, so I talked instead. I knew it sounded good. I could hear it.

So I tried to break into the UK music scene, but there is a lot of competition. I was just 16, and every disappointment knocked my confidence – three years is a long time when you're not making money. I made some headway, met a producer and signed up with a booking agent. I even had a single, Fallen Out, which made it to number two in the Official UK Urban Charts about two years ago, but after a year the hype died down.

I wasn't going to give up that easily, so I made a plan. I thought, where can I go where there's nobody quite like me, a young British white rapper? It wasn't random – I did my research. And it worked. I signed a management deal in Belgium, and got some sponsorship and label support. It's all been pretty recent.

The weird thing is, I've only been out to Belgium three times. The third time I went was for the Ostend Big Live festival last year, which was amazing – girls were holding up signs saying, "I love Taylor." I'd be lying if I said I didn't like the attention. I do. It's cool.

I did a signing session after the festival, and the fans were going absolutely crazy, climbing over fences to get to me, throwing things, screaming my name. I couldn't help thinking that people back in my home town wouldn't even believe me if I told them. I probably wouldn't mention it, though. I'd rather just be me, Taylor. That's the benefit of being famous somewhere else. You get to come back down to earth.

Putting it into practice

2 Read **Source 1**. Explain what you learn about Taylor Jones.

Remember to:

- show your understanding by explaining in your own words
- support your ideas using the text. *(8 marks)*

When you tackle this kind of question in the exam, remember to:

- spend around 12 minutes answering it
- read the source text carefully
- use your skills of inference to select points that are relevant to the question
- select short quotations to support your ideas.

Remember: You will have more space than this to answer the question in the exam. Use your own paper to finish your answer to the question above.

Connotations

Connotations are the ideas or attitudes that a word or phrase suggests to the reader.

Read the opening of the newspaper article below (**Source 1**), then answer Question 1.

Source 1

THE NEW GLOBAL ADDICTION: SMARTPHONES

Who would have thought, 20 years ago, that a plastic and glass box smaller than the palm of your hand would ruin the good manners of millions of people?

Yes, we know about the digital miracles brought about by the smartphone. But there's no more powerful measure of its growing influence on our lives than the sudden shattering – in less than a decade – of standards of behaviour dating back centuries.

Imagine two 1950s housewives meeting for tea and pastries in a department store. One of them is chirping about some teak dining room chairs that she thinks her husband will adore. But the other woman, instead of nodding politely, fishes her diary out of her handbag and flicks through its pages with glazed eyes. That would be the last time those ladies met for tea, I fancy.

These days, in contrast, many of Britain's 30 million smartphone owners think nothing of surreptitiously checking Twitter during a conversation. Younger smartphone users have mastered the art of texting one person while talking to another. You need only travel on the top of a London bus to see virtuoso demonstrations of this trick by teenagers.

1 Which ideas and attitudes might the two circled words in the text suggest to the reader?

Draw a line between the circled words and their possible connotations.

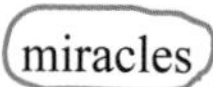

obsession drugs reliance magic religion

Guided

2 Choose one of the circled words from Question 1. Write two sentences commenting on the connotations of this word.

The word .... has connotations of ....

....

This suggests that ....

....

3 Pick one more word from the article above which the writer has chosen for its connotations.

You could pick (shattering) (chirping) (virtuoso) or one of your own.

Write one or two sentences commenting on the word's connotations and its effect.

....

....

....

....

Rhetorical devices 1

Read the extract from the online article below (**Source 1**), then answer Questions 1 and 2.

Source 1

Time to let the furry friends go

My daughter is nearly 12. This month she graduated to secondary school and resolved to put childish things behind her. To that end, she lined up her entire menagerie of soft toys on the sofa, five deep, to make a considered, contemplative decision about which of them was going to get the chop.

There were bears, geese, rabbits, dogs, hedgehogs, pigs, elephants, a penguin, two tigers and a single doll, a scraggy female item named, for some reason, Bob. The toys had all featured in her life at one time or another. Large ones, small ones. Sucked ones, chewed ones. Loved ones, unloved ones. Nameless ones.

And now they were huddling together on the sofa like the proud, uncowering victims of a firing squad.

I walked into the living room to see all this just as my daughter, who sat facing them, removed a cupping hand from her chin. She looked solemn.

'What's going on?' I said.

'I'm just deciding which ones to "let go",' she replied, supplying the quote marks with her fingers, and went back to her thinking. For a moment I felt almost physically sick. 'You can't do that!' I said, and then thought, why the hell not? They're hers.

'Why not?' she said. 'They're mine. And besides, I've looked after them all these years. I can do what I want with them.'

I had no answer to that. But it didn't stop me from feeling uneasy.

I told myself that it was because I was upset at the spectacle of my daughter cutting herself away so ruthlessly from her infancy. But I knew that I was not facing up to the whole truth.

1 How many of the following rhetorical devices can you identify in the article? Look for at least **three**, and circle them.

- alliteration
- repetition
- emotive language
- rhetorical question
- lists
- a short sentence

2 For each device you identified, write one or two sentences commenting on:

- why the writer has used it
- the effect the writer wants to have on the reader.

....

....

....

....

....

....

....

....

....

....

....

Had a go ☐ Nearly there ☐ Nailed it! ☐

Rhetorical devices 2

Read the extract from the online article below (**Source 1**), then answer Questions 1 and 2.

Source 1

Battery-farmed puppies are a shame on our nation

We are a nation of dog lovers. Or are we?

Linda Goodman is a truly committed dog lover. So much so that, in an attempt to draw attention to the plight of battery-farmed dogs, she has chosen to live like a breeding bitch. A live webcam has been filming her suffering for five days so far. But so far, very few people have paid her much attention.

When we talk of puppy farming, you might imagine it could be quite picturesque – adorable photogenic pups gamboling in paddocks. But it's actually grotesque.

There are estimated to be 5,500 breeding bitches living in council-approved licensed kennels in just three counties of Wales. They will never know the love of a human being, never sit on a sofa, go for a walk, play fetch or have that spot on their tummies tickled that will make their back leg twitch. Enslaved to a breeding schedule, they're just locked in a barn for years and years, left to stand in their own mess – often in the dark – until their litter size falls to an unprofitable size, at which point they are put to sleep.

Why? Because we buy their pups. Their misery will continue until the trade is either banned or it becomes unprofitable. The poor pups, meanwhile, are destined for dealers and pet shops. It's a gamble if they even survive the journey or their first few weeks. The life of a battery-farmed dog is cheap. Their poor rearing, lack of socialisation and lack of health tests can make them expensive for their owners, though.

The Kennel Club estimates one in five of us have bought a puppy-farmed dog. Linda in the shed knows all this. That's why she's locked herself in.

So what can you do to get Goodman and all those poor dogs out of the shed? Write to your MP. And resist the temptation of that puppy in the window, so that it becomes unprofitable to trade in misery.

1 How many of the following rhetorical devices can you identify in the article? Look for at least **three**, and circle them.

- rhetorical question
- lists
- contrast
- repetition
- emotive language
- pattern of three

2 For each device you identified, write one or two sentences commenting on:
- why the writer has used it
- the effect the writer wants to have on the reader.

....

....

....

....

....

....

....

....

Figurative language

Read **Source 1** below, then answer Question 1.

An answer that **comments on the effect** of figurative language is much stronger than one that simply says 'It's a simile' but that does not comment on its effect.

Source 1

A POOR SCHOOL REPORT IS NO BARRIER TO SUCCESS

I hope there are a few red faces at Eton this week. The school prides itself on turning out pupils who will shine in later life, but it made a pig's ear of educating the biologist Professor Sir John Gurdon, who has just been awarded the Nobel Prize (for medicine) for his pioneering work in the field of cloning.

It would be 'a sheer waste of time' for Gurdon to pursue a career in science, wrote his teacher, a Mr Gaddum, in a withering end-of-term report in 1949. He wouldn't listen, couldn't learn simple biological facts and, horror of horrors, 'insisted on doing work in his own way'. In one test, Gurdon scored a miserable 2 out of 50.

1 The writer uses the word 'shine' **figuratively**. What does this metaphor suggest?

....

....

....

Now read the rest of the text, then answer Questions 2 and 3.

One wonders how many other pupils Mr Gaddum and his ilk put off with their caustic one-liners.

Sir John certainly isn't the first high achiever to have had buckets of cold water poured over him by his teachers. 'He will never amount to anything,' predicted a Munich schoolmaster in 1895, failing to spot the potential in the young Albert Einstein. Gary Lineker's teacher warned: 'He must devote less of his time to sport if he wants to be a success – you can't make a living out of football.'

These days, thank goodness, the pendulum has swung the other way. I savoured my daughters' school reports. 'Clara is a legend,' wrote her chemistry teacher when she was 15. Her confidence rocketed – until she compared notes with her friends and found there had been five legends in one class.

Some parents worry that today's schoolchildren would benefit from a few home truths. But they shouldn't miss the obvious moral of Sir John's story. Growing children need encouragement like a plant needs water.

2 Identify at least one more metaphor from the article. Write one or two sentences commenting on why the writer has used it and its effect on the reader.

....

....

....

3 Identify the simile the writer has used in the article. Write one or two sentences commenting on why the writer has used it and its effect on the reader.

....

....

....

Putting it into practice

Read the extract from a newspaper article below (**Source 1**), then have a go at the exam-style question opposite.

Source 1

JUST ONE LITTLE TATTOO

I stand in the kitchen smiling from ear to ear, because he's home – our student son is home and the family is together again. And after supper, after the washing up is done, the others – his younger siblings – drift off to watch television, and he says: 'Would you like to see my tattoo?'

I say, 'You're joking.'

He says, 'No, I'm not.'

But still I wait. Any minute he's going to laugh and say,'You should see your faces' because this has been a running joke for years, this idea of getting a tattoo – the hard man act, iron muscles, shaved head, Jason Statham, Ross Kemp. He's a clever boy. Maybe during his school years he thought a tattoo would balance the geeky glory of academic achievement.

His father says, 'Where?'

'On my arm,' he says, and touches his bicep through his shirt.

His lovely shoulder.

In the silence, he says, 'I didn't think you'd be this upset.'

After a while, he says, 'I thought about it. I went to a professional. It cost £150.'

£150? I think, briefly, of all the things I could buy with £150.

'It's just a tattoo,' he says, when the silence goes on so long that we have nearly fallen over the edge of it into a pit of black nothingness.

His father asks, 'Does it hurt?'

'Yes,' I say, cutting across this male bonding. 'It does. Very much.'

For three days, I can't speak to my son. I can hardly bear to look at him. The last thing we need, I think, is an explosion of white-hot words that everyone carries around for the rest of their lives, engraved on their hearts. In any case, I'm not even sure what it is I want to say. In my mind's eye I stand there, a bitter old woman with pursed lips wringing my hands. He's done the one thing that I've said for years, please don't do this. It would really upset me if you did this. And now it's happened. So there's nothing left to say.

I know you can't control what your children do. Why would you want to, anyway? If you controlled what they did, you'd just pass on your own rubbish tip of imperfections. You hope the next generation will be better, stronger, more generous. I know all you can do as a parent is to pack their bags and wave as you watch them go.

So I cry instead. I have a lump in my throat that stops me from eating. I feel as if someone has died.

Putting it into practice

3 How does the writer use **language features** to **describe** and **explain** her feelings?

Remember to:

- give some examples of language features to describe
- give some examples of language features to explain
- explain the effects.

(12 marks)

When you tackle this kind of question in the exam, remember to:

- spend around 18 minutes answering it
- read the source text carefully, highlighting any effective language choices
- support all your points with evidence and a clear explanation focusing on **effect**.

Remember: You will have more space than this to answer the question in the exam. Use your own paper to finish your answer to the question above.

Had a go ☐ Nearly there ☐ Nailed it! ☐

Identifying sentence types

Look at the sentences below, then answer the questions that follow.

A My hands were trembling.

B Even though I had done this hundreds of times before, I was still terrified.

C My blood ran cold and my heart stopped.

D Blind terror.

1 Look carefully at the four sentences above. Each one is a different type of sentence. But which is which?

Sentence .... is a simple sentence.

Sentence .... is a compound sentence.

Sentence .... is a complex sentence.

Sentence .... is a minor sentence.

2 Now look at an extract from a newspaper article (**Source 1**). Highlight or circle one example of each kind of sentence: simple, compound, complex and minor.

Source 1

Life's a lottery but sometimes the good guys win

Adrian and Gillian Bayford won £148 million on the lottery. An incredible sum. Staggering. Riches beyond all compare. What does such an amount of dosh even look like?

Despite the life-changing sum, the couple have said they are determined to remain grounded. That's what they all say.

Yet after announcing their Euromillions triumph, the couple from Haverhill in Suffolk decided to take a small holiday. Was it to be the usual dash to Dubai?

No. The couple flew on easyJet to Scotland, and then travelled to Carnoustie on the east coast.

Remember:

- a SIMPLE sentence contains **one verb**, giving **one piece of information** about an event or action
- a COMPOUND sentence contains **two or more verbs**, giving **two or more pieces of information** about events or actions; they are connected with **and** or **but** or **then**
- a COMPLEX sentence contains **two or more verbs**, giving **two or more pieces of information** about events or actions joined with a range of connecting words, such as **because**, **although**, **if** and several others
- a MINOR sentence is grammatically incomplete because it does not contain a verb.

Commenting on sentence types

Read the extract from Ben Fogle's autobiography below (**Source 1**), then answer Questions 1 and 2.

Source 1

The accidental adventurer

Shadows danced across the canvas like fiendish ghouls. Their long, clawed fingers scratched menacingly against the fabric. I lay rigid as a gentle breeze snapped at the loose skirt of my tent.

My arms were stretched down my sides, soldier-like, and I lay on my hands to stop them trembling.

What the hell was that deafening noise reverberating around the tent? I held my breath again, but the pounding continued. It was my heart racing with fear. Each beat creating a thunderous din.

I felt faint. This was it. The sleeping bag began to vibrate to the beat of my heart. I had never been so scared in my entire life.

1 The extract begins with two short, simple sentences that describe the scene. What kind of mood do these short sentences create?

....

....

....

2 The extract ends with a series of very short, simple sentences. How do these add to the mood which the writer has created?

....

....

....

Read on, then answer Question 3.

I had to make a run for it. My life depended on it. I needed to wait for the right moment and run as fast as I could. Quietly I eased my body from the bag. My heart began to race even faster.

I'd taken risks, but it was never meant to end like this. Here. Now. I still had so much I wanted to achieve. I hadn't even had a chance to say goodbye.

Guided

3 In this extract, the writer uses a mixture of simple, compound and minor sentences. Write one or two sentences about the effect each of these sentence types creates.

The writer uses several simple and short compound sentences to ....

....

....

....

The use of minor sentences ....

....

....

....

Had a go ☐ Nearly there ☐ Nailed it! ☐

Making the best comments

Read the extract from a university student's online blog below (**Source 1**), then answer Questions 1 and 2.

Source 1

Is your Facebook page a lie?

When I started university, people told me: 'These will be the best days of your life.' I was leaving my snoozy town in the countryside and heading towards the sparkle of the big city to study fashion journalism at the London College of Fashion. Not only would these be the best days of my life, everyone said, but also they would be the most glamorous.

They couldn't have been more wrong. By the end of my first year I was seriously considering dropping out. I had not made as many friends, had as much fun, or enjoyed my course as much as I thought I was going to. My shoulders sagged with the weight of my disappointment, and I blamed myself. 'I chose this. Is it my fault I am not living the university dream?' I felt sad and desperately lonely. But I didn't tell anyone.

I certainly didn't put it on Facebook – its culture of competitive sharing made me feel even worse. Scrolling through my friends' feeds, it was clear they were having a ball. Jemma Lamble and I are friends on Facebook – what impression did she get from my profile? 'There is one feeling I got when I clicked on your Facebook and that is jealousy. You looked like you were really enjoying yourself.'

1 Look at the different kinds of comments which one student made on the extract above. Which is which? Draw lines from the type of comment to the correct answer.

1 Comment on viewpoint	**A** The short sentence 'They couldn't have been more wrong' brings the build up of excitement to a sudden end.
2 Comment on purpose	**B** The writer vividly and honestly describes the impact which her disappointment had on her.
3 Comment on language choice	**C** The writer's excitement at heading to university is suddenly undermined when she reveals that it turned out to be a great disappointment.
4 Comment on sentence structure	**D** The writer's disappointment makes the reader feel sorry for her.
5 Comment on the effect on the reader	**E** The word 'sparkle' contrasts with 'snoozy' building up the reader's expectations, making the writer's disappointment seem even greater.

2 Look again at **Source 1**. Make **two** further comments on the text. Aim to make two different kinds of comment – e.g. on purpose and sentence structure.

....

....

....

....

....

Comment on language and purpose: argue and persuade

Read the extract from a newspaper article below (**Source 1**), then answer Question 1.

Source 1

I'd risk my life to rescue my dog; that's just what owners do

Every winter there are stories of dog owners who have died trying to save a dog that has fallen through ice. People who have no pets of their own often listen to such stories with dismay. Why would anyone risk their life trying to save a dog? I would. Your dog's part of your family, and part of your life. You love it. If you have no family, partner or children, you possibly love your dog even more. It's your companion: a reason to get up in the morning. Your life revolves round it, and if you see it in any sort of serious trouble, then you will, usually, try and save it, just as you would try and save anyone else that you love.

Guided

1 In the extract, the writer uses a rhetorical question followed by a very short sentence. Think about how these language techniques support the writer's argument, and the effect she wants to have on the reader. Write one or two sentences explaining your ideas.

The rhetorical question engages the reader, inviting them to

....

....

The short sentence answers the question clearly and bluntly. The effect of this is ....

....

....

Read the final paragraph of the article, then answer Question 2.

I am not expecting that this will convince anyone who's never had a dog. Many people are outraged if you compare an animal to a child. But if a helpless creature that you love is in serious trouble, possibly about to die, it doesn't really matter if it's a dog, a cat, a horse or a beached whale. You're going to go on jumping into rivers, oceans, fights and fires to save it, whatever anyone else thinks.

2 Identify examples of the following language techniques in the paragraph above. Write one or two sentences commenting on the effect of each one.

(a) emotive language: ....

....

....

(b) a list: ....

....

....

Comment on language and purpose: describe

Read the travel writing extract below (**Source 1**), then answer Question 1.

Source 1

Bondi Beach

It is 5.45am. In the dim pre-dawn light a hooded figure slips silently by. He is barefoot and carries a large flat board under his arm. With head bowed, he is walking purposefully. I follow. He pads down the main street under the fig trees, past a row of shops and cafés not yet open.

The hooded man is gliding on and I quicken my pace. Already I can hear the sound of the ocean. We make our way down the stone steps, past the memorial to the Australian dead of two world wars, across the promenade and on to the soft sandy beach. The surf is rolling in. The young man, now bare chested, is running down the beach, splashing through the waves and swimming out. The sea is studded with flotsam, as though a ship has been wrecked. I look again and realise that the black debris is scores of surfers waiting on their boards like praying mantises.

This is Bondi Beach, Australia. The air is still cool and as the sun rises it seems the whole beach begins to move, gyrating and pumping in a fitness frenzy.

Runners, sleek as panthers, are pacing along the promenade and, on the grass, muscles are expanding and contracting rhythmically in the green gym. In the pool at the southern end of the beach swimmers pound up and down in training. This is the other face of Bondi, one of Sydney's most fashionable beaches, which you have to rise early to witness.

1 How many of the following features of **descriptive writing** can you identify in the extract?

(a) Describing using the five senses.

(b) Figurative language – e.g. simile, metaphor.

(c) Language choice.

(d) The writer's feelings.

Guided

2 Choose two of these features including the simile underlined. Write one or two sentences about each one, commenting on the writer's choice and its effect on the reader.

The writer uses a simile to compare the waiting surfers with praying mantises. This suggests

....

....

....

....

....

....

....

Comment on language and purpose: inform and explain

Read the extract from a newspaper article below (**Source 1**), then answer Question 1.

Source 1

Having friends and going swimming are more important than money to today's youth

In their world of mobile phones, the latest fashions and, of course, Facebook, this may be a tough sell to your stroppy teenager. But it seems it really is the simple things in life that will make them happy.

According to new research, children aged 10–15 gain an increased sense of well-being by having friends around for tea, going swimming and a secure home life rather than a steady flow of money.

Guided

1 How would you describe the tone of this article: formal or informal? Write one or two sentences using evidence from the text to support your ideas.

The tone of the article is ....

....

....

This tone is created through the writer's choice of language – for example, ...

....

....

Read more of the article, then answer Question 2.

Children in families with a lower income were no less happy than those with higher-earning parents, says a study by the Institute for Social and Economic Research at the University of Essex. It found that using the Internet can be beneficial, but only for up to an hour a day as anything more can affect important social activities.

Girls aged between 10 and 12 are the happiest group of children, while those aged 12–15 are the least happy.

Eating five portions of fruit and vegetables a day is also important, the research found.

2 How has the tone of the article changed in these paragraphs? Why has it changed? Write one or two sentences using evidence from the text to support your ideas.

....

....

....

3 Which of these key features of information and explanation writing can you identify in the extract?

(a) Facts and statistics.

(b) Connective such as **first**, **then**, **next** help to signal the structure of the text.

Write down an example of any that you find, then write a sentence commenting on their effect on the reader.

....

....

....

Putting it into practice

Read **Source 1** below, then have a go at the exam-style question opposite.

Source 1

'You are inferior, you will be exterminated!'

It was not the friendliest welcome to a family day out but my 13-year-old son was lapping it up. We were at the new home of the Doctor Who Experience in Porth Teigr, Cardiff Bay, a cyberman's shuffle from BBC's Roath Lock Studio where the television series is filmed.

With help from the current Doctor Who (Matt Smith) directing us via specially shot footage, we had experienced flying the TARDIS, trooped past Weeping Angels and were now up against the Doctor's shrieking arch enemy the Daleks. And after a spot of three-dimensional time tunnelling we managed to escape into part two of the Experience, the largest collection of Doctor Who props and related exhibits ever assembled.

Did the Experience do justice to the world's longest-running science fiction television programme? My son thought it was supersonically awesome, whereas down-to-earth dad enjoyed it but felt there was room for improvement.

The walk-through section was sensibly restricted to 35 visitors at a time, and was well paced, lasting a decent 25 minutes, but some of the technical effects were a tad tame compared to the lavish attractions at Legoland, or the benchmark technology of the 4D *Marvel* movie at Madame Tussauds.

The static exhibition was more rewarding, packed full of enough detail to engross the occasional armchair viewer (me) and satisfy a hardcore Whovian (my son). I loved the scientific seriousness outlining the evolution of the sonic screwdriver.

Besides operating a Dalek there isn't much interactivity, although there are plenty of monsters, robots and a life-sized Doctor Who to be photographed next to.

It has a well balanced amount of behind-the-scenes displays to convey the skilled work that goes into the programme without breaking the sci-fi spell.

The inevitable shop at the end of the show is manageable and if you can avoid paying £250 for a Matt Smith tweed jacket the overall experience is good value for money.

Putting it into practice

3 How does the writer use **language features** to **inform** the reader about the Doctor Who experience and to **describe** his visit?

Remember to:
- give some examples of language features to inform
- give some examples of language features to describe
- explain the effects.

(12 marks)

When you tackle this kind of question in the exam, remember to:
- spend around 18 minutes answering it
- read the source text carefully, highlighting any effective language choices
- support all your points with evidence and a clear explanation focusing on EFFECT.

Remember: You will have more space than this to answer the question in the exam. Use your own paper to finish your answer to the question above.

Identifying presentational devices 1

Look at the webpage below.

1 Look at the labels around the webpage. Draw a line from each one to an example of that presentational feature on the webpage.

Guided 2 Underneath each label, write one or two sentences commenting on:

(a) the effect of the feature on the reader

(b) how it helps the text achieve its purpose and get the writer's viewpoint across.

Fonts

The designer has chosen this font because ....

....

....

....

Headings

....

....

....

....

....

Putting your child first.

Visiting our hospital

Orchard Place Hospital for Children

Hospital | Charity

Patients | Parents | Staff | News | Vacancies

Your visit | Your care | Your life

Do your bit!

Orchard Place Hospital Charity

Find more information

search

Colour

....

....

....

....

....

....

Images

....

....

....

....

....

....

Logo

....

....

....

....

....

....

Identifying presentational devices 2

Look at the webpage below.

1 Look at the labels around the webpage below. Draw a line from each one to an example of that structural feature on the webpage.

Guided

2 Underneath each label, write one or two sentences commenting on:

(a) the effect of the feature on the reader

(b) how it helps the text achieve its purpose and get the writer's viewpoint across.

News | Weather | Sport | Politics | Search

UK footballers paid 1,500% more than 20 years ago

Footballers have seen their wages rise by over 1,500% over the past 20 years, compared to the 186% increase in the average UK wages, according to a new study.
Research from the High Pay Centre shows that top players have seen bumper pay rises, while those playing for lower division have seen their pay rise by significantly less.

The High Pay Centre research also revealed the impact of these wages on fans, saying they are the ones 'paying the price' of excessive pay:

- the lowest ticket available has increased by over 1,000% since 1989
- the cheapest ticket to watch Liverpool has increased from £4 to £45
- English clubs account for approximately 56% of all debt in top flight clubs across Europe – despite only representing 2% of clubs
- over half of English football league clubs have been insolvent in the past 20 years.

Premier League Wage Bills 2010–2011	
Chelsea	£191 million
Manchester City	£174 million
Liverpool	£135 million
Arsenal	£124 million

Nick Isles, Chair of the High Pay Centre said the figures show it is 'time to put the brakes on this dramatic escalation in pay at the top'.

Bullet points

The writer has used bullet points to make the text appear clearer to the reader.

Tables

Sections/boxes

Paragraphs

Had a go ☐ Nearly there ☐ Nailed it! ☐

Using P-E-E to comment on presentational devices

Look carefully at the presentational and structural features of the newspaper article below (**Source 1**), then answer the questions that follow.

Source 1

The dogs who listen to children reading

Scheme aims to encourage children to read aloud

Some children show the dog the pictures as they read.

When children read to him, Danny does not criticise or correct their pronunciation. He just nods and pricks up an ear, although sometimes he closes his eyes and appears not to be listening.

Danny is a dog and a novel way of encouraging pupils at Oakhill primary school in Tamworth, Staffordshire, to read aloud.

1 Look at these six extracts from one student's comments on presentation. Organise them into two Point-Evidence-Explanation paragraphs – for example, B, A, C, F, E, D.

A The headline connects the words 'dogs', 'listen' and 'reading' which is surprising, amusing and intriguing.

B Together the headline and the subheading summarise the article but they spoil the surprise that the writer has tried to create in the opening paragraph of the article: the reader has already guessed that Danny is a dog before the writer reveals it.

C The subheading adds further information to the headline.

D The headline attracts the reader's attention, not only because it is in a large, bold font, but also because of its choice of language.

E It explains the intentions of the scheme to 'encourage' reading aloud.

F The writer uses this surprising summary to capture the reader's interest, encouraging them to read the article and discover more. It also suggests that the article will be humorous.

....

Guided

2 Write a Point-Evidence-Explanation paragraph explaining how the image in **Source 1** is effective.

The image shows a child reading a book on grass with a white dog

Like the headline, this is surprising because dogs don't usually listen to humans and have human like qualities. Also because humans and dogs don't communicate properly.

Commenting on headlines

Look at the headlines below.

A

How do I look? Electrifying!
Fancy dress shocker ends in hospital
A man dressed as a Christmas tree got more of a shock than he bargained for when he tried switching on the Christmas lights he had used to decorate his costume.

B

Success story
Self-published ebook hits the bestseller list
A LANCASHIRE HOUSEWIFE has become one of the most successful ebook authors of all time.

C

Tiny ideas for tiny minds
Politicians are constantly underestimating voters' intelligence
Politicians' desperate attempts to communicate with voters are frequently based on an assumption that most of us are complete idiots.

D

Would you trust a politician?
Survey shows public trust in our MPs at an all time low

1 Which headlines have withheld information? A, B, C

2 Which headlines use alliteration? B / C

3 Which headlines use repetition? C - repetition is same word

4 Which headlines use a rhetorical question? D / A

5 Which headlines reflect the tone of the article that follows? ~~A B~~ D

6 Which subheadings add more detail to the story? A / C / B / D

Guided 7 Choose two of the headlines above. Write one or two sentences about each one, commenting on:
(a) any significant features (b) their effect on the reader (c) how they link with the text.

Headline ~~B~~ D uses a rhetorical question to ~~persuades~~ inform the reader about the level of trust people have for MP's and makes the reader concerned.

The effect of this is to evoke ~~sarcasm~~ guilt. It is linked to the text as it tells the reader what the text would be about.

Had a go ☐ Nearly there ☐ Nailed it! ☐

Image and effect

Read the headline and opening sentence of the newspaper article below (**Source 1**), then answer the questions.

Source 1

School dinners: still not pulling in the punters

Despite numerous campaigns, policies and celebrity appeals, a significant number of school canteens are still failing to attract their target audience: school kids. Fed at home on a diet of nuggets and chips, is it any wonder that kids' eyes aren't lighting up at the sight of school broccoli?

1 Which image would you choose to illustrate this article? (Circle **A**, **B**, **C** or **D**.)

A

B

C

D

Write one or two sentences explaining your choice of image. Aim to comment on:

- why you feel the image supports the point of view expressed in the newspaper article
- the effect you hope the image will have on the reader.

A – It shows food children wouldnt eat

Comparing the presentation of two source texts

Look carefully at **Sources 1** and **2** below, then answer the questions that follow.

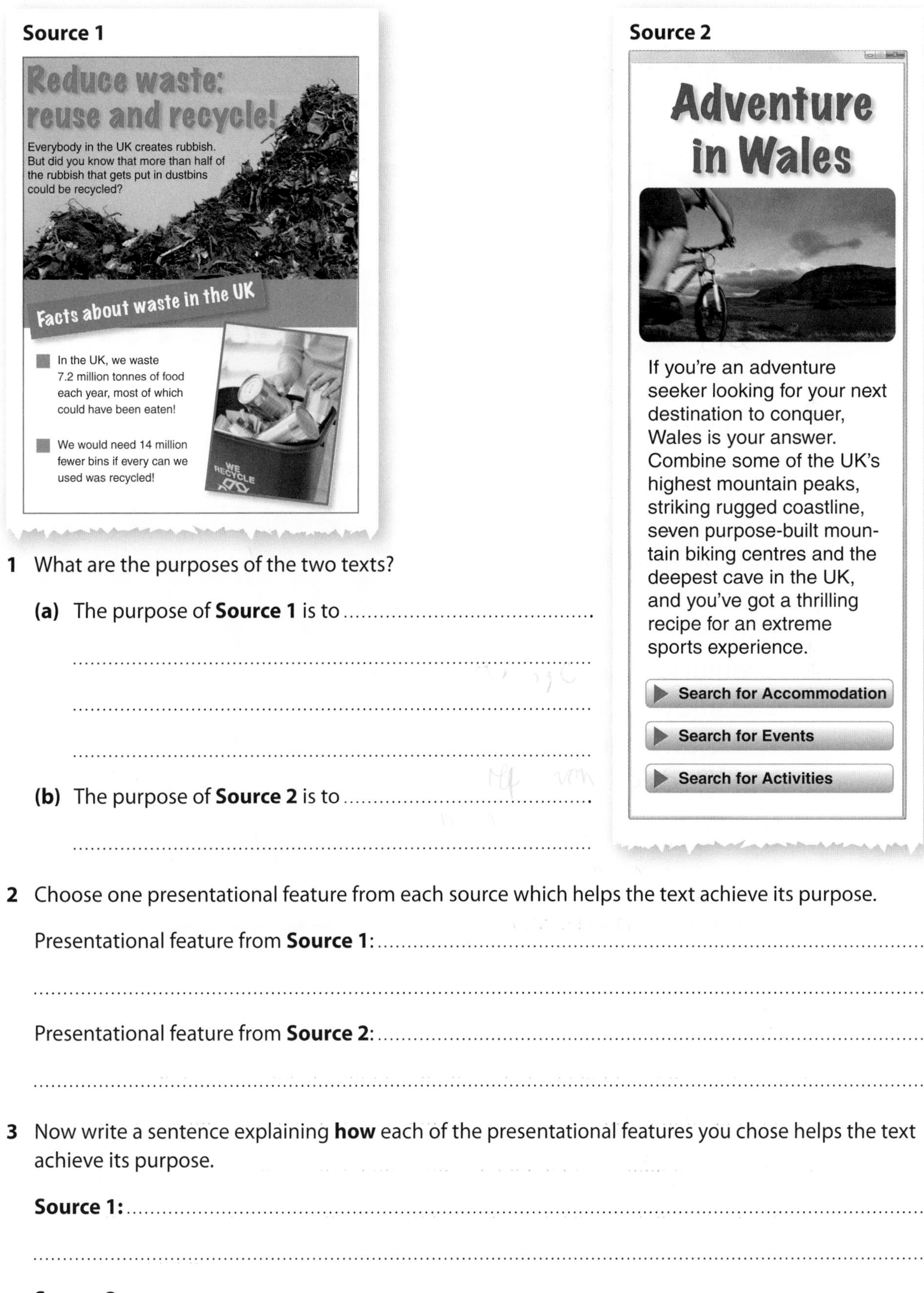

Source 1
Reduce waste: reuse and recycle!
Everybody in the UK creates rubbish. But did you know that more than half of the rubbish that gets put in dustbins could be recycled?
Facts about waste in the UK
In the UK, we waste 7.2 million tonnes of food each year, most of which could have been eaten!
We would need 14 million fewer bins if every can we used was recycled!
WE RECYCLE
Source 2
Adventure in Wales
If you're an adventure seeker looking for your next destination to conquer, Wales is your answer. Combine some of the UK's highest mountain peaks, striking rugged coastline, seven purpose-built mountain biking centres and the deepest cave in the UK, and you've got a thrilling recipe for an extreme sports experience.
Search for Accommodation
Search for Events
Search for Activities

1 What are the purposes of the two texts?

(a) The purpose of **Source 1** is to ....

....

....

....

(b) The purpose of **Source 2** is to ....

....

2 Choose one presentational feature from each source which helps the text achieve its purpose.

Presentational feature from **Source 1**: ....

....

Presentational feature from **Source 2**: ....

....

3 Now write a sentence explaining **how** each of the presentational features you chose helps the text achieve its purpose.

Source 1: ....

....

Source 2: ....

....

Putting it into practice

Look closely at **Source 1** below, then have a go at the exam-style question opposite.

Source 1

ABOUT US | WATER PROJECTS | GET INVOLVED | CONTACT

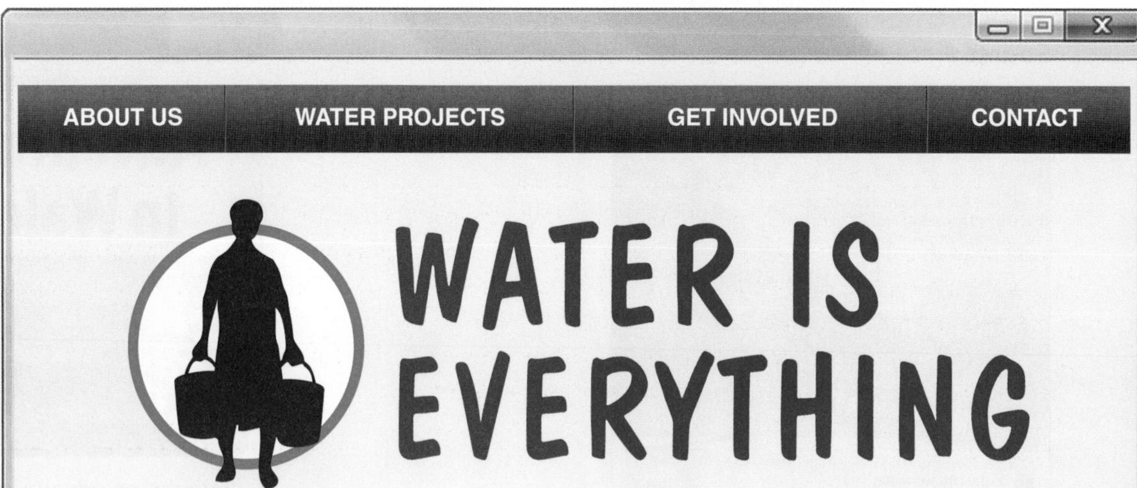

Water and health

Dirty water kills more people than the number of people killed in war and violence each year. Diarrhoea and dysentery, which are illneses caused by dirty water, are particularly harmful to young children.

DONATE

Getting water

Many women and children in countries in Africa spend much of their day walking miles to their nearest water source. This water is often dirty and will make them ill.

Putting it into practice

4 Look at **Source 1**. Write about the way that the text uses **presentational features** for effect.

Remember to:

- write about the way the source is **presented**
- explain the **effect** of the presentational features
- write about the way the source **looks**.

(12 marks)

When you tackle this kind of question in the exam, remember to:

- spend around 18 minutes answering it (note that in your exam you will be asked to **compare** the ways in which presentational features are used in two texts; use this question to practise writing about presentation in just **one** text)
- look closely at the source text, highlighting any effective presentational features
- **choose** three or four presentational features to focus on
- **explain** the **effect** of each feature on the reader.

Remember: You will have more space than this to answer the question in the exam. Use your own paper to finish your answer to the question above.

Had a go ☐ Nearly there ☐ Nailed it! ☐

Planning to compare presentation

Read **Sources 1** and **2** below, then complete Question 1.

Source 1

Do you think I'm made of money?

The phrase revealed as most popular among Britain's penny-pinching dads

It is a phrase familiar to many a teenage girl who has turned to the 'bank of dad' when in need of extra cash for a night out or a new outfit. Now 'Do you think I'm made of money?' has topped a poll of the most frequently used sayings among Britain's dads – followed closely by 'money doesn't grow on trees'.

A total of 43 per cent admit to using the phrases they heard their dad say while they were growing up. Far from ignoring their dads' words of wisdom, 73 per cent said they now appreciated all the fatherly advice.

CHANGE THE RECORD DAD! FATHERS' TOP 10 MOST-USED PHRASES

1. Do you think I'm made of money?
2. Money doesn't grow on trees.
3. He's as thick as two short planks.
4. When I was your age …
5. I'm not sleeping; I'm just resting my eyes.
6. I'm not going to tell you again.
7. Were you raised in a barn?
8. Don't talk back to your mother.
9. If you were told to jump off a cliff, would you?
10. They don't make them like they used to.

Source 2

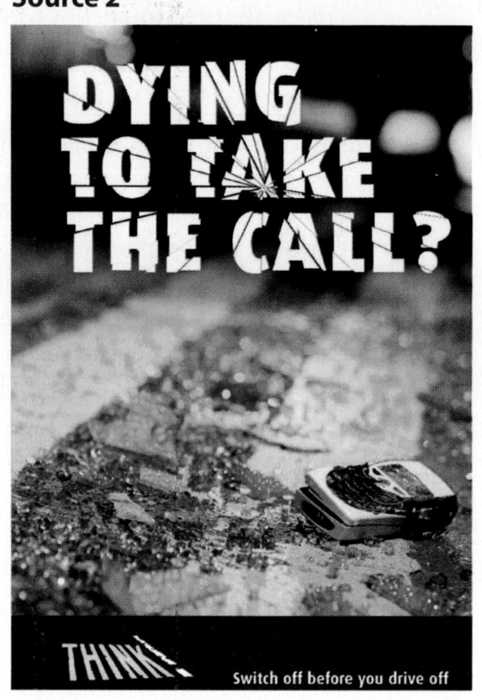

1 Look at one student's plan for comparing the presentational features and their effect in the two source texts. Add as much detail to the plan as you can, including points, evidence and explanations.

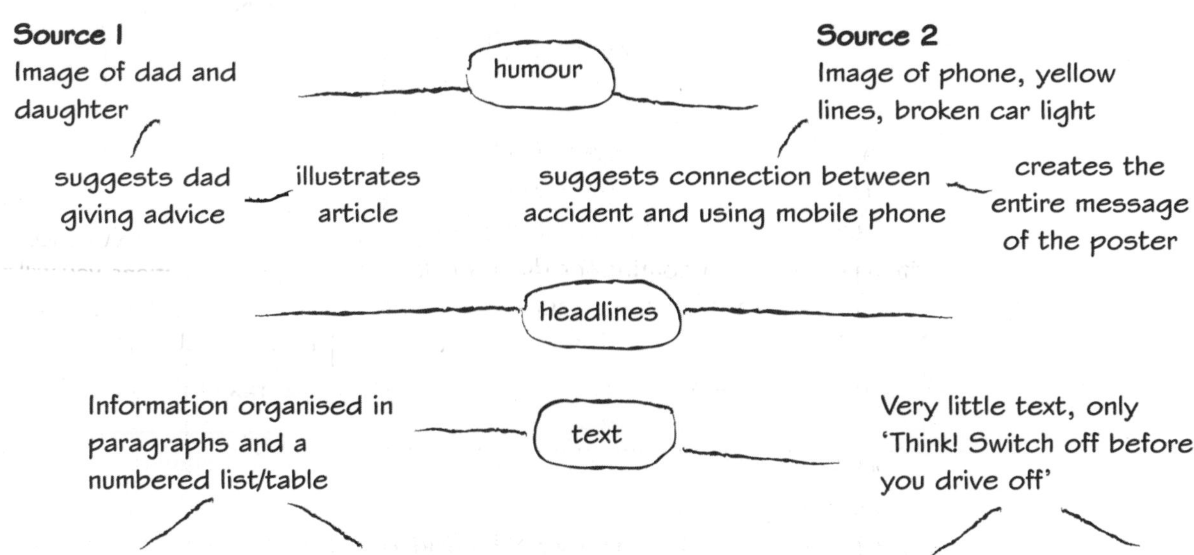

Answering a compare question

When you compare the presentation used in two texts you can write about:

The content: what the texts are about

Both texts are about ...

On the other hand, **Source 2** explores ...

Source 1 is about ...

The purpose: what they aim to achieve

The purpose of **Source 1** is to ...

One way it achieves this is through its language choice. For example, ...

Source 2 aims to ...

The presentation achieves this through the use of ...

inform

explain

argue

describe

persuade

entertain

The effect on the reader:

Both texts grab the reader's attention but in different ways.

Source 1 engages the reader by ...

Source 2, however, uses ...

create humour

intrigue

influence

shock

encourage sympathy

Similar presentational features:

Both texts use images, but use them to achieve different effects.

Source 1 uses the image to ...

Source 2 uses its image to ...

illustrate

reflect the tone of the text

make a point

1 Look again at the two texts on page 46. Use the prompts above to write a paragraph comparing the different ways in which presentational features are used for effect in the two texts. Remember to support your ideas with evidence and an explanation of its effect.

....

....

....

....

You need to support your points on presentation with evidence. Instead of using quotations, you will need to describe the presentation feature you are writing about, e.g.

The image shows a mobile phone in the road.

The headline is presented in a font which makes the writing look like shattered glass.

Putting it into practice

Look closely at **Source 1** and **Source 2** below, then have a go at the exam-style question opposite.

Source 1

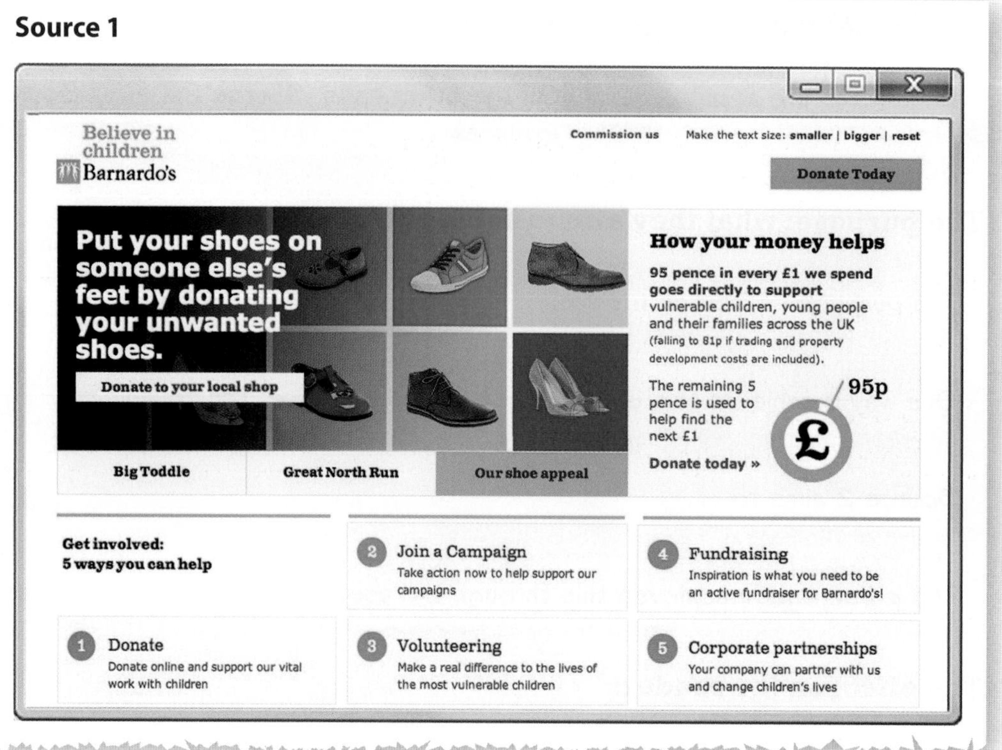

Source 2

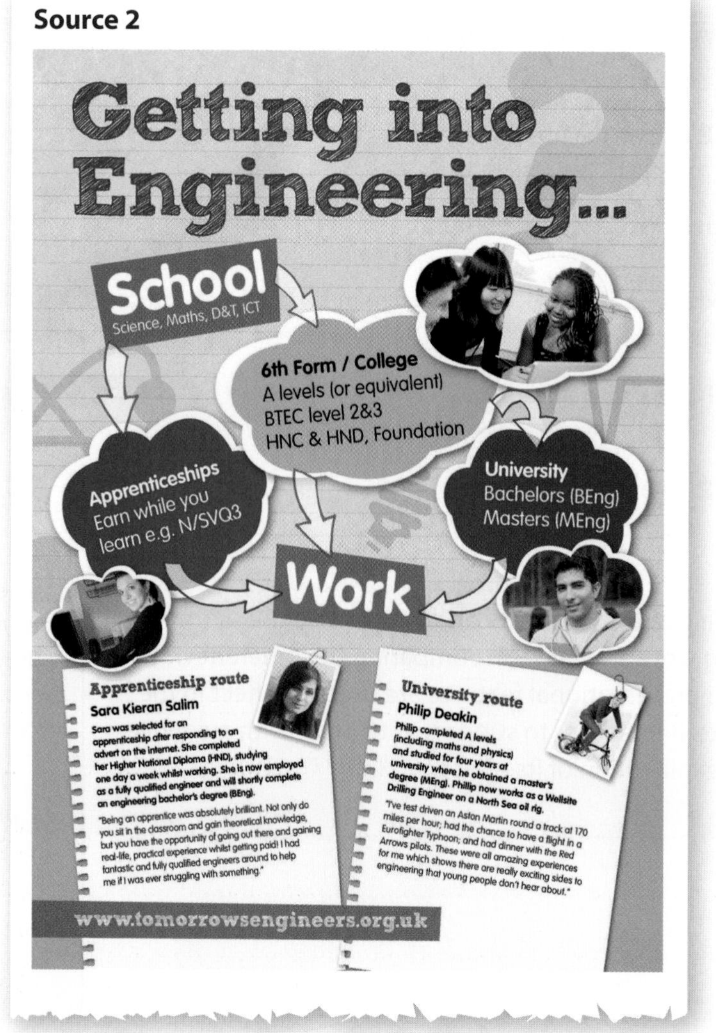

Putting it into practice

4 Look at **Source 1** and **Source 2**. Compare the way that both texts uses **presentational features** for effect.

Remember to:

- write about the way the sources are **presented**
- explain the **effect** of the presentational features
- compare the way they **look**.

(12 marks)

When you tackle this kind of question in the exam, remember to:

- spend around 18 minutes answering it
- look closely at the source text, highlighting any effective presentational features
- **choose** two or three presentational features to focus on in each text
- **explain** and **compare** the **effect** of each text's presentational features on the reader.

Remember: You will have more space than this to answer the question in the exam. Use your own paper to finish your answer to the question above.

Had a go ☐ Nearly there ☐ Nailed it! ☐

Reading the questions

Look closely at the exam-style question below, then answer Questions 1–4.

> **5** A national newspaper is running a competition inviting school and college students to write an **article** for a series entitled 'School days are the happiest days of your life'. Write an **article** in which you **describe** a school day you particularly enjoyed.
>
> Remember to:
> - write an **article**
> - use language to **describe**. *(16 marks)*

1 (a) Circle the words in the question that suggest the **audience** you should be writing for.

(b) Write a description of the audience you should write for.

....

....

2 Circle the words that tell you the **purpose** your writing should achieve.

3 Circle the words in the question that tell you the **form** in which you should write your answer.

4 Circle the words that tell you the **topic** you should write about.

Now look at another exam-style question, then answer Question 5.

> **6** 'All students should complete at least one month's paid work experience before they leave school'. Write a **letter** to your head teacher, **arguing** for or against this point of view.
>
> Remember to:
> - write a **letter**
> - use language to **argue**.
>
> Try to write approximately two sides of your answer booklet. *(24 marks)*

5 Circle the words in the question that:

(a) suggest the **audience** you should be writing for.

(b) tell you the **purpose** your writing should achieve.

(c) tell you the **form** in which you should write your answer.

(d) tell you the **topic** you should write about.

Read each question carefully, taking note of:
- audience (e.g. adults, students, parents, etc.)
- purpose (e.g. explain, persuade)
- form (e.g. newspaper article, letter)
- topic.

The questions and planning your exam time

In the **Writing** section of your exam you will answer two questions.

- Question 5 asks you to complete a piece of writing to **inform, explain or describe**.
- Question 6 asks you to complete a piece of writing to **persuade** or **argue** a point of view.

Look at the exam-style paper below, then answer the questions that follow.

Section B: Writing

Answer **both** questions in this section.

You are advised to spend about one hour on this section.

---

5 A national newspaper is running a competition, inviting school and college students to write an article for a series entitled 'School days are the happiest days of your life'. Write an **article describing** a school day which you particularly enjoyed.

Remember to:

- write an **article**
- use language to **describe**.

Try to write approximately one side of your answer booklet. *(16 marks)*

6 'All students should complete at least one month's paid work experience before they leave school'. Write a **letter** to your head teacher, **arguing** for or against this point of view.

Remember to:

- write a **letter**
- use language to **argue**.

Try to write approximately two sides of your answer booklet. *(24 marks)*

1 How long should you spend in total on your answer to Question 5? .... minutes

2 How long should you spend in total on your answer to Question 6? .... minutes

3 Complete the table below, writing in the number of minutes you should spend on the three vital stages of answering each question.

How long should you spend ...	Question 5	Question 6
planning your answer to each question?	.... minutes	.... minutes
writing your answer to each question?	.... minutes	.... minutes
checking your answer to each question?	.... minutes	.... minutes

Check the number of marks each question is worth. It will help you to get an idea of how long you should spend on each question.

Had a go ☐ Nearly there ☐ Nailed it! ☐

Writing for an audience

1 Look at the two exam-style tasks below. Which audience are you being asked to write for?

A

6 'Technology is taking over our lives. We need to spend less time staring at screens and more time talking to each other.' Write an **article** for your school or college website **arguing** for or against this point of view.

Remember to:

- write an **article**
- use language to **argue**. *(24 marks)*

The audience for this task is ....

B

5 A local newspaper is inviting entries for a writing competition, asking young writers to write an extract from their autobiography. Write your **entry**, **describing** a memorable event in your life.

Remember to:

- write a **competition entry**
- use language to **describe**. *(16 marks)*

The audience for this task is ....

2 Think about the kind of language you would use in your answer to Question A above. Which of the opening sentences below would be the most appropriate for this audience? Write one or two sentences explaining your answer.

(a) Some of us spend half our lives gawping at laptops and the telly which I reckon is just like such a waste of time.

(b) When you see a teenager staring at a computer, do not assume that they are wasting their time.

....

....

3 Think about the kind of language you would use in your answer to Question B above. Which of the opening sentences below would be the most appropriate for this audience? Write one or two sentences explaining your answer.

(a) When I was about seven, the most amazing thing happened.

(b) Well, the funniest thing I remember from when I was little was the time when my brother really lost his rag with me.

....

....

4 Choose one of the exam-style questions above. Write the first two or three sentences of your answer, focusing on using the most appropriate language for your audience.

....

....

Writing for a purpose: inform and explain

Look at the exam-style question below, then answer the questions that follow.

> **5** Many people have a role model – a person whose achievements and attitude they admire. Write an **article** for your school or college website, **explaining** who your role model is and why you admire them.
>
> Remember to:
>
> - write an **article**
> - use language to **explain**.
>
> *(16 marks)*

Guided

1 Writing that informs or explains often uses subheadings. Write down up to five subheadings that you could use to organise your answer to the exam-style question above.

1 What's so great about ....?

2 ....

3 ....

4 ....

5 ....

2 Writing that informs or explains often uses facts and statistics to support its ideas and make the reader feel the information is reliable and trustworthy. Write down five facts or statistics that you could include in your writing about your chosen role model.

1 ....

2 ....

3 ....

4 ....

5 ....

3 Writing that informs or explains usually uses a formal tone. It makes your writing seem more reliable and trustworthy. Write the opening paragraph of your response to the exam-style question above. Aim to:

- use a formal tone
- include some of the facts and statistics you used in your answer to Question 2.

....

....

....

....

....

....

....

Writing for a purpose: describe

Look at the exam-style question below, then answer the questions that follow.

5 A local interior design company are running a competition asking people to write about their ideal home for their new brochure. Write an **entry describing** your ideal home.

Remember to:

- write a **competition entry**
- use language to **describe**. *(16 marks)*

1 Using the five senses can help you to create a vivid image in the reader's mind. Choose one room in your ideal home, then complete the table below to gather ideas you could use in your writing.

In this room, I can ...

see:	
hear:	
smell:	
touch:	
taste:	

2 Figurative language will also help you to create a strong description. Focus on one object in your chosen room. Write one or two sentences, describing it with either a simile, a metaphor or personification.

....

....

3 **(a)** How does being in this room make you feel? ....

....

....

(b) When you feel frightened, you might feel shaky, or sick or sweaty. How does the feeling you chose in Question 3 (a) actually **feel**? Write down three examples:

Example 1: ....

Example 2: ....

Example 3: ....

4 Using some of your answers to Questions 1, 2 and 3, write the first three sentences of your answer to the exam-style question above.

....

....

....

Writing for purpose: argue and persuade

Look at the exam-style question below, then answer the questions that follow.

6 'The Internet is an addictive and harmful drug.' Write an **article** for a magazine of your choice, **arguing** for or against this point of view.

Remember to:

- write an **article**
- use language to **argue**. *(24 marks)*

1 When you write to argue, you need **at least three** key points to support your argument. Write down **three** points in support of your argument, either for or against this point of view.

Point 1: ....

Point 2: ....

Point 3: ....

2 You will need to select evidence to support each of your key points. Write down one piece of evidence to support each of the three ideas you noted in your answer to Question 1.

Evidence for Point 1: ....

Evidence for Point 2: ....

Evidence for Point 3: ....

Evidence can be any of these things:

- a fact or statistic – e.g. It is estimated that over 60% of the UK use the Internet every day.
- expert opinion – e.g. Psychiatrists are starting to offer treatment for Internet addiction.
- an example from your own experience – e.g. I know several people who spend every hour of their evenings and weekends on the Internet.

3 Look at the rhetorical devices below. These devices can make an effective argument more powerful:

- rhetorical questions
- direct address
- repetition
- emotive language
- alliteration
- contrast
- patterns of three
- lists
- hyperbole.

Now write **two** sentences that you could include in your answer to the above exam-style question using a rhetorical device in each one.

Sentence 1: ....

....

Sentence 2: ....

....

Guided

4 A counter-argument allows you to identify an argument that people might use to disagree with your point of view – which you can then dismiss. What point might people on the opposing side of this argument make? How could you dismiss it? Write your ideas down.

It could be argued that ....

....

However, ...

....

Putting it into practice

Look closely at the exam-style paper below, then answer the questions that follow.

Section B: Writing

Answer **both** questions in this section.

You are advised to spend about one hour on this section.

---

5 Your school or college website is publishing a series of articles entitled 'The most important thing I learned at school'. Write your **article**, **explaining** the most important thing you learned at school and why you think it is important.

Remember to:
- write an **article**
- use language to **explain**. *(16 marks)*

6 'Men and women can never be equal.' Write an **article** for your local newspaper, **arguing** for or against this point of view.

Remember to:
- write an **article**
- use language to **argue**. *(24 marks)*

1 How long will you spend on each question?

Q5: .... minutes

Q6: .... minutes

Guided

2 Read the questions on the exam paper very carefully, then complete the table below.

	Audience	Purpose	Form	Topic
Question 5	teachers / students			
Question 6		argue		

3 Note down some of the key features you should remember to use in each question.

Question 5: Key features	Question 6: Key features

Form: letters and emails

Look at the extract from an exam-style question below, then complete Questions 1 and 2.

> **6** Write a **letter** to the head of your school or college, **arguing** for or against changing the school uniform.
>
> Remember to:
> - write a **letter**
> - use language to **argue**. *(24 marks)*

1 It is important to use the correct layout at the beginning and end of a formal letter. Add the following features, correctly laid out, to the letter below:

- your address
- the address of the person you are writing to
- the date
- the salutation (Dear …)
- the sign off (Yours …)
- your signature
- your name.

I am writing regarding your recent letter to parents and students, dated 13 September

and hope you will consider this before making any decision.

2 Which layout features would you **not** need to include if you were asked to write a formal email to the head of your college or school?

....

....

Had a go ☐ Nearly there ☐ Nailed it! ☐

Form: articles

Look at the exam-style question below, then answer the questions that follow.

6 'Many people find teenagers frightening or threatening – and with good reason.' Write an **article** for your local newspaper which **persuades** your readers that this statement is right or wrong.

Remember to:

- write an **article**
- use language to **persuade**. *(24 marks)*

1 Think of a title you could use as your article's **headline**.

....

....

Headlines use a range of techniques including: repetition, a rhetorical question, alliteration, a pun or a rhyme.

2 Think of a **subheading** that will add more information to your headline.

....

....

....

3 Write your opening paragraph, summing up your ideas in two or three sentences.

....

....

....

....

....

....

4 Articles often include quotations from 'experts' to support the writer's ideas. You may need to make this up in the exam! Who could you quote in this article? What will they say?

....

....

....

....

5 Write your closing paragraph concluding your article with your views on the statement.

....

....

....

....

....

Form: information sheets

Read the exam-style question below, then answer the questions that follow.

> **5** Write an **information sheet**, **informing** visitors about one aspect or feature of your local area.
>
> Remember to:
> - write an **information sheet**
> - use language to **inform**. *(16 marks)*

1 Think of two different aspects or features of your local area that you could write about. Then choose the best one.

Aspect/feature 1: ....

Aspect/feature 2: ....

2 Your information sheet will need a title to grab and engage the interest of your readers. Think of **two** possible titles for your information sheet. Then choose the best one.

Title 1: ....

Title 2: ....

3 Organising your writing under subheadings can help guide the reader – and help you to plan your writing. Write down three subheadings you would use in your information sheet.

Subheading 1: ....

Subheading 2: ....

Subheading 3: ....

4 Information sheets often use a range of structural features to present information more clearly and appealingly. Which of the following could you include in this leaflet? Write a sentence explaining how you would use them.

Bullet pointed or numbered list: ....

....

Table: ....

....

Chart: ....

....

Text box: ....

....

Putting it into practice

Answer the exam-style question below, focusing in particular on audience, purpose and form.

6 'Students work hard all day at school. They should not have to do homework as well.' Write a **letter** to the head of your school or college, **persuading** them that this statement is right or wrong.

Remember to:

- write a **letter**
- use language to **persuade**.

Try to write approximately two pages in your answer booklet. *(24 marks)*

When you tackle any writing question in the exam, remember to:

- be sure about the audience, purpose, form and topic for your writing
- include all the relevant key features of form and purpose
- plan your writing before you start
- check your spelling, punctuation and grammar thoroughly when you have finished writing.

Remember: You will have more space than this to answer the question in the exam. Use your own paper to finish your answer to the question above.

Planning an answer: describe

Look at the exam-style question below, then answer Question 1.

5 Choose a memorable trip or holiday you have enjoyed and **describe** it in an **article** for a travel website.

Remember to:
- write an **article**
- use language to **describe**. *(16 marks)*

1 Complete the stages of planning outlined below.

Stage 1: Decide which trip or holiday you will describe. Write it in the centre of the spidergram below.

Stage 2: You will need to write two or three paragraphs for your answer. Decide what you will include in each one. Add your ideas to the spidergram below.

Your idea **does not** have to be action packed.
It **does not** have to be true.
It **does** have to be written interestingly and engagingly.

Stage 3: Add some detail for each of your planned paragraphs. Think about how you could use:
- the five senses: see, hear, smell, touch and taste
- your feelings
- details to create mood or atmosphere
- language for effect.

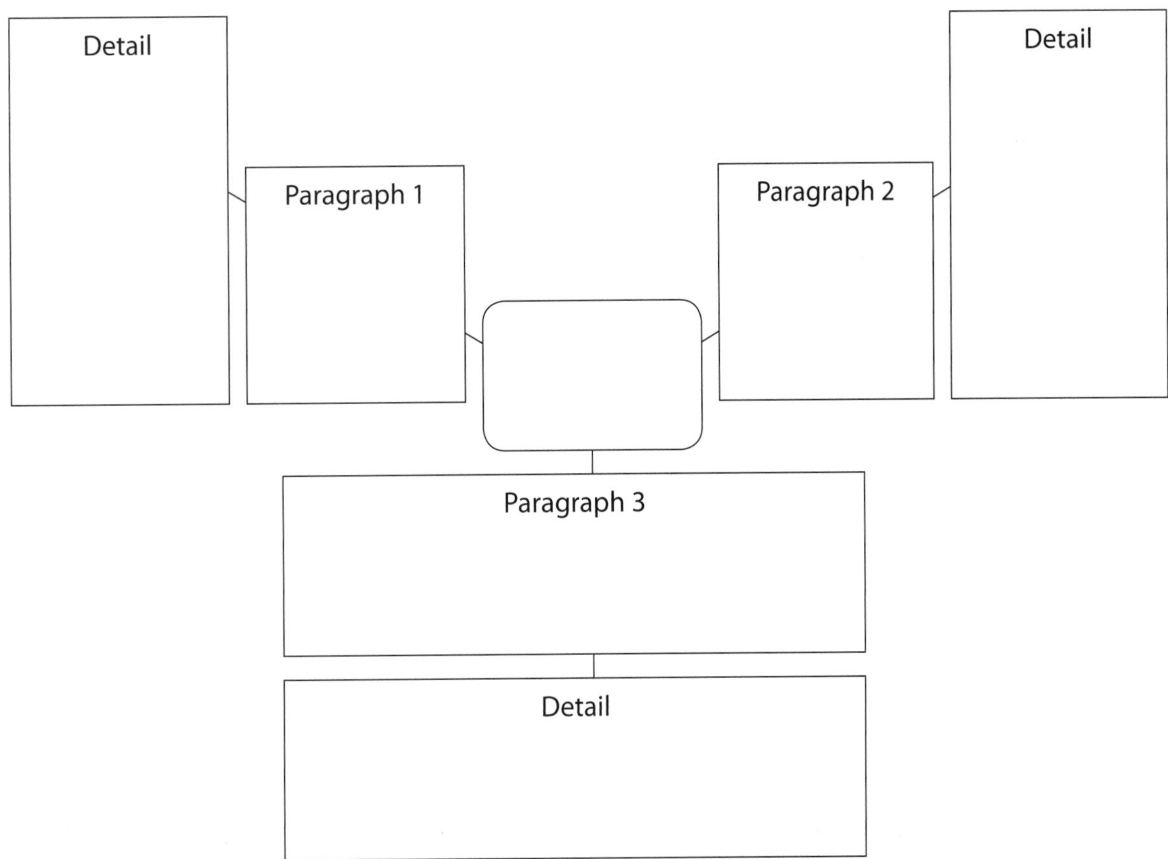

Remember:
- you only have **25 minutes** to plan, write and check this task – so aim for two or three paragraphs of well-crafted writing
- quality is rewarded; quantity is not.

Had a go ☐ Nearly there ☐ Nailed it! ☐

Planning an answer: inform or explain

Look at the exam-style question below, then answer Question 1.

5 A new TV series 'Britain's Best Teacher' is looking for great teachers. Write a **letter** to the producers, **explaining** why one of your teachers should appear on the programme.

Remember to:

- write a **letter**
- use language to **explain**. *(16 marks)*

1 Complete the stages of planning outlined below.

Stage 1: Decide which teacher you will write about. Write their name in the centre of the spidergram below.

Stage 2: To guide your reader, plan an introduction which tells them what are you writing and why they should read it. Add it to the spidergram.

Stage 3: You will need to write two or three paragraphs for your answer. Decide on the key points you will include in each one. You could think of them as subheadings which will help to organise your writing.

Stage 4: Sequence your key points by numbering them. What would be the most logical or effective order?

Stage 5: Add some ideas and details to each of your key points.

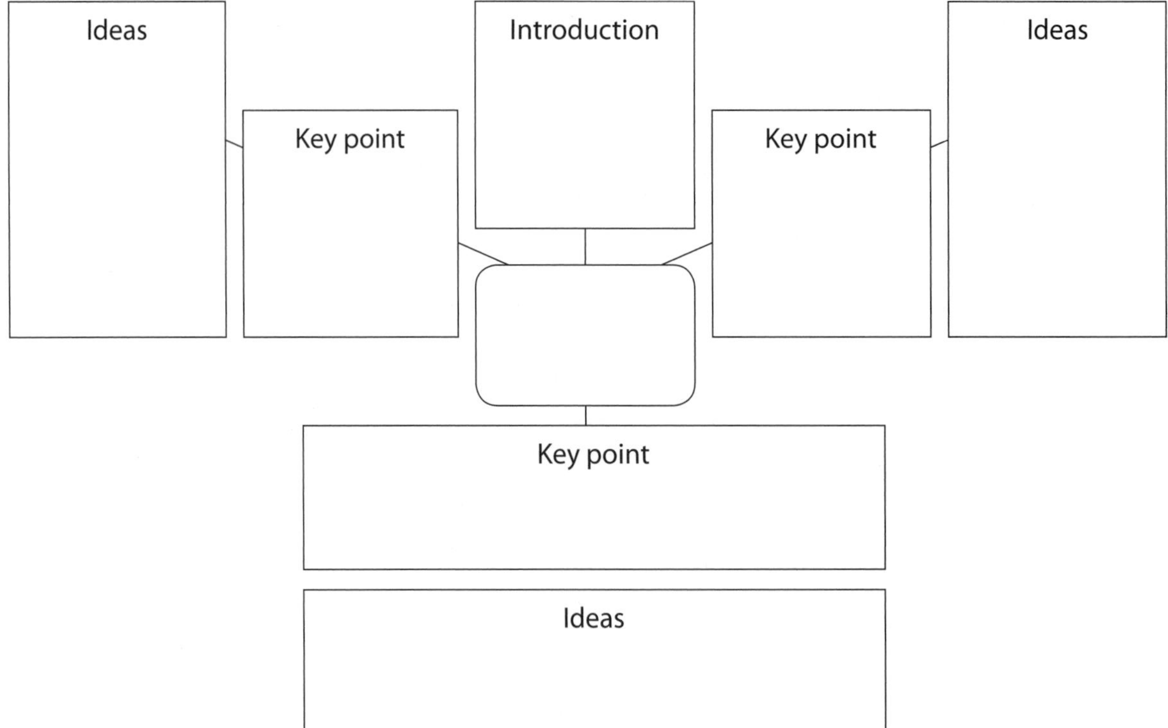

Remember:

- you only have **25 minutes** to plan, write and check this task – so aim for two or three paragraphs of well-crafted writing
- quality is rewarded; quantity is not
- you will not always include subheadings when you write an information or explanation text – but you can still use them to help you plan your writing.

Planning an answer: argue or persuade

Look at the exam-style question below, then answer Question 1.

> **6** 'GCSEs do not give a fair or accurate picture of a student's real skills and abilities.' Write an **article** for your school or college website **arguing** for or against this point of view.
>
> Remember to:
> - write an **article**
> - use language to **argue**. *(24 marks)*

1 Complete the stages of planning outlined below.

Stage 1: Decide whether you agree or disagree with the point of view in the question. Summarise your response in the centre of the spidergram below.

Stage 2: To guide readers, plan an introduction that tells them what are you writing and why they should read it. Add it to the spidergram.

Stage 3: Decide on two or three key points you will make.

Stage 4: Decide on the evidence you will use to support your key points.

Stage 5: Sequence your key points by numbering them. What would be the most logical or effective order?

Stage 6: Add a counter-argument to your plan. What might someone who disagrees with you say? How can you prove their argument to be wrong?

Stage 7: Plan a conclusion that will hammer your point of view home.

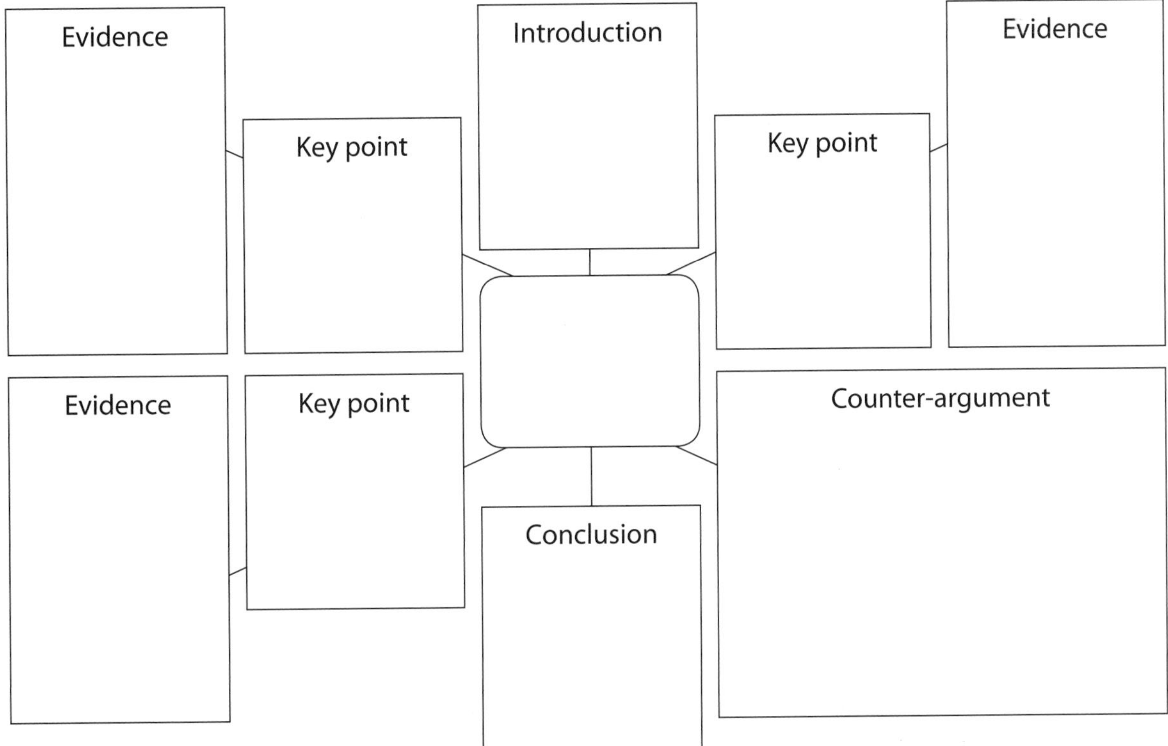

> Remember:
> - you only have **35 minutes** to plan, write and check this task – so aim for five or six paragraphs of well crafted writing
> - quality is rewarded; quantity is not.

Had a go ☐ Nearly there ☐ Nailed it! ☐

Beginnings

Look at the exam-style question below, then complete the questions that follow.

6 'Schools and colleges should give students more careers advice to help them make the best choices.' Write an **article** for a magazine of your choice **arguing** for or against this view.

Remember to:

- write an **article**
- use language to **argue**.

(24 marks)

1 The first sentences of your writing must grab the reader's attention and make them want to read on. Try writing the opening sentence of your response to the exam-style question above in lots of different ways:

Using a rhetorical question: ....

....

Making a bold or controversial statement: ....

....

With a relevant quotation: ....

....

With a shocking or surprising fact or statistic: ....

....

With a short, relevant, **interesting** anecdote: ....

....

2 Choose one or two of your ideas from Question 1 and write the rest of your introduction to the exam-style question above. Remember your introduction needs to introduce:

- the topic you are writing about
- your point of view.

....

....

....

....

....

....

....

Remember: Don't tell the reader what you are going to be writing in your article:

In this article I am going to argue that ... ✗

Just write it!

Endings

Look at the exam-style question below, then complete the questions that follow.

> **6** 'Schools and colleges should give students more careers advice to help them make the best choices.' Write an **article** for a magazine of your choice **arguing** for or against this view.
> Remember to:
> - write an **article**
> - use language to **argue**. *(24 marks)*

1 The final paragraph or **conclusion** of your writing should make a lasting impression. Try writing sentences you could include in your conclusion to the above exam-style question, using these techniques.

End on a vivid image: ....

....

End on a warning: ....

....

End on a happy note: ....

....

End on a thought-provoking question: ....

....

End on a 'call to action': ....

....

Refer back to your introduction, but don't repeat it: ....

....

2 Choose one or two of your ideas from Question 1 and write your conclusion to the exam-style question above.

....

....

....

....

....

....

....

....

....

....

....

> Avoid introducing your conclusion with phrases like:
> - In conclusion …
> - To summarise …

Putting it into practice

Plan your answer to the exam-style question below.

6 'If the universe is infinite, there must be alien life out there somewhere.' Write an **article** for your school or college website **arguing** for or against this point of view.

Remember to:

- write an **article**
- use language to **argue**.

Try to write approximately two pages in your answer booklet. *(24 marks)*

When you tackle any writing question in the exam, remember to:

- be sure about the audience, purpose, form and topic for your writing
- spend 3–5 minutes gathering ideas
- organise and sequence your ideas
- plan how you will introduce and conclude your writing.

Remember: You will have more space than this to answer the question in the exam. Use your own paper to finish your answer to the question above.

Paragraphing

Look at the exam-style question below, then answer the questions that follow.

> **6** 'Schools and colleges should give students more careers advice to help them make the best choices.' Write an **article** for a magazine of your choice **arguing** for or against this view.
> Remember to:
> - write an **article**
> - use language to **argue**. *(24 marks)*

1 Look at the paragraph below. It is an extract from one student's response to the exam-style question above.

> When students choose their GCSE options in Year Nine, they do not always choose subjects because they will help them in their future career. I chose my GCSEs either because I liked the teacher or because lots of my friends had chosen that subject. Neither of these are good reasons. With more advice, students would make more sensible decisions.

This student has organised the paragraphs in her argument using Point-Evidence-Explain. Identify and label the three different sections of this paragraph: **point**, **evidence** and **explain**.

2 Plan your own Point-Evidence-Explain paragraph in answer to the above exam-style question.

Point: ....

Evidence: ....

Explain: ....

3 Now write the paragraph you have planned in full.

....

....

....

....

....

....

....

....

....

4 Identify and label the three different sections of your paragraph: **point**, **evidence** and **explain**.

5 Plan a second Point-Evidence-Explain paragraph in answer to the above exam-style question.

Point: ....

Evidence: ....

Explain: ....

> Each time you start a new point, start a new paragraph.

Had a go ☐ Nearly there ☐ Nailed it! ☐

Using connectives

1 Different connectives have different purposes. Copy the list of connectives below into the table, adding each one to the correct column.

Because
Consequently
Especially
For example
For instance
Furthermore …
However
In addition …
In particular
In the same way
Moreover …
Not only … but also
On the other hand
Significantly
Similarly
Such as
Therefore
… whereas …

Adding an idea	Explaining	Illustrating	Emphasising	Comparing	Contrasting

2 Look at the paragraphs below. They are extracts from one student's writing on the topic

… exams do not give a fair or accurate picture of a students' real skills and abilities.

Fill in all the gaps using appropriate connectives.

Many students are very successful in areas which exams do not or cannot assess. ……………………, one student at my school runs his own business designing websites for local companies. This is not something he has learned at school and …………………… his success will not be reflected in his exam results.

……………………, some students' success depends not on hard work but on natural ability. …………………… this has more impact on less academic students. One student, ……………………, might achieve an A grade with little or no hard work, while another might have worked really hard for years to achieve a C.

…………………… there is no obvious alternative to exams as a measure of students' ability.

3 Now write your own Point-Evidence-Explain paragraph in response to the above exam-style question. Remember to use a range of connectives to guide the reader through your argument.

Look back at your planning on page 63 to help you.

……………………………………………………………………………………………

……………………………………………………………………………………………

……………………………………………………………………………………………

……………………………………………………………………………………………

Putting it into practice

Answer the exam-style question below, focusing in particular on paragraphing and using connectives.

5 What do you think is the greatest invention in the history of mankind? Write an **article** for your school or college website, **explaining** the invention you have chosen and why you chose it.

Remember to:

- write an **article**
- use language to **explain.**

Try to write approximately one page in your answer booklet. *(16 marks)*

When you tackle any writing question in the exam, remember to:

- write in paragraphs
- plan one point per paragraph
- use connectives to guide your reader through the text.

Remember: You will have more space than this to answer the question in the exam. Use your own paper to finish your answer to the question above.

Had a go ☐ Nearly there ☐ Nailed it! ☐

Getting the right tone

Look at the two exam-style questions below, then answer the questions that follow.

A 6 'Computer games are a waste of time.' Write an **article** for your school or college website, **arguing** for or against this view.

Remember to:
- write an **article**
- use language to **argue**. *(24 marks)*

B 6 'Computer games are a waste of time.' Write an **article** for a teenage gaming website, **arguing** for or against this view.

Remember to:
- write an **article**
- use language to **argue**. *(24 marks)*

1 Who is the audience for Question A? ....

2 What kind of tone should you use to appeal to this audience? ....

....

3 Who is the audience for Question B? ....

4 What kind of tone should you use to appeal to this audience? ....

....

5 Look at the sentences below. Which have a tone that would be appropriate for which exam question? Label each sentence either 'A', 'B', or 'N' (for neither).

Point of view: first or third person

Many people think that computer games are designed to empty young people's minds and fill their time.

I think computer games have helped me a lot over the years.

Formal or informal

It could be argued that some games not only improve the player's problem-solving skills but, played with other people online, can also develop teamwork skills.

It's only oldies and people who don't know their Xbox from their Wii that come up with this sort of argument.

Standard English or non-standard English

What is wrong with switching off your brain and turning on your games console?

There ain't nothing like a session on yer favourite shoot em up to chill you out.

6 Write one or two sentences in response to each of the exam-style questions above.

A ....

....

B ....

....

Formal and informal language, standard English, slang, humour and point of view can all affect the tone of your writing. Think about the audience you are writing for and make your choice.

Synonyms

1 Look at the sentence below. Think of **at least two** synonyms (words with a similar meaning) for each circled word.

Synonyms for 'students':

1 ....

2 ....

3 ....

Synonyms for 'improve':

1 ....

2 ....

3 ....

Students can improve their learning by doing more revision.

Synonyms for 'learning':

1 ....

2 ....

3 ....

Synonyms for 'doing':

1 ....

2 ....

3 ....

If you get stuck, use a thesaurus – but first **try** to use the large vocabulary that you already have in your head. **Remember:** You won't have access to a thesaurus in the exam.

2 Look at each of the words in the table below. Complete the table adding at least two synonyms for each word.

embarrassed	**upset**	**scream**	**moment**	**annoyed**

3 Now write a paragraph in response to the exam-style question below. Aim to use some of the vocabulary from your answer to Question 2.

5 Your school or college is inviting entries for a writing competition. The topic is 'My most embarrassing moment'. Write your **entry, describing** a time when you were embarrassed.

Remember to:

- write a competition **entry**
- use language to **describe**. *(16 marks)*

....

....

....

....

....

....

....

Had a go ☐ Nearly there ☐ Nailed it! ☐

Choosing vocabulary for effect: describe

1 Look at this description.

> The sun's glorious golden rays burst through my gleaming windows, sending shimmering sparkling beams of incandescence dancing around my walls.

Rewrite the above description in **eight** words or fewer. You could re-use some of the original vocabulary or use some of your own ideas.

....

....

2 Look again at your answer to Question 1. Compare your shorter sentence with the longer original version. Which do you prefer? Write a sentence explaining why.

....

....

....

Now look at the exam-style question below, then answer Questions 3 and 4

> **5** Lots of people have a favourite place. Write an **article** for a travel website, **describing** what you think is 'The greatest place on earth'. It could be somewhere abroad, in the UK, or even in your local area.
>
> Remember to:
> - write an **article**
> - use language to **describe**. *(16 marks)*

3 Write two or three sentences in which you begin to describe what you consider to be the 'greatest place on earth'.

....

....

....

....

....

4 Look again at your answer to Question 3. Have you included enough description? Or too much? Do you need to add more? Or should you cross some out?

5 Look again at your improved answer to Question 3. Circle three words that you think could be improved. Write down three synonyms for each word, then choose the most effective one.

....	....	....
....	....	....
....	....	....

Choosing vocabulary for effect: argue and persuade

Guided

1 Look at the sentences below. Rewrite them, using emotive language to add more impact.

(a) usually? frequently? barbarically? cruelly? destroyed? slaughtered?

Animals in laboratories are ~~often~~ treated ~~really badly~~ and then ~~put to sleep.~~

(b) If we continue to use too many of the earth's resources, the world will not have enough food.

(c) Our lives are filled with computers. We may not like it but we cannot do much about it.

2 Look at this sentence:

Some parents greeted the school's controversial plans with a (cry) of disapproval.

What would be the impact of replacing the circled word with roar ? How would the connotations of roar affect the reader's response to the sentence? Write one or two sentences explaining your ideas.

....

....

....

3 What would be the impact of replacing the circled word with whimper ?

....

....

4 Write the opening two or three sentences of your answer to the exam-style question below. Aim to choose vocabulary for its impact and its connotations.

> **6** 'Social networking is a waste of time.' Write an **article arguing** for or against this view.
> Remember to:
> - write an **article**
> - use language to **argue**. *(24 marks)*

....

....

....

Had a go ☐ Nearly there ☐ Nailed it! ☐

Language for effect 1

1 Look at the extracts from students' writing below. Some are taken from a piece of descriptive writing, some from a piece of argument writing. Connect the rhetorical device to the extracts in which it is used.

- contrast
- rhetorical question
- repetition
- list

A Why was he staring at me like that?

B How would you feel if it were your beloved dog or cat being treated in this way?

C Some people carefully sort their rubbish into recycling bins, separating their metal, card, paper, plastic and glass. Most people just chuck it all in one big bin.

D As the phone rang, the bright sunshine disappeared, swallowed up by a wall of rolling dark clouds.

E I stared at the crowd in front of me: thin people, fat people, tall people, short people, old people, young people. I recognised none of them.

F The only solution which we should consider, the only solution which the human race can offer, the only solution which we can all contribute to, is right under our noses.

2 Now look at the exam-style question below. Write **up to four** short extracts from your answer, using **one or more** of these language techniques in **each**.

> **6** 'Many adults see teenagers as a problem – but it isn't the teenagers that need to change. It's the adults.' Write an **article** for a magazine of your choice, **arguing** for or against this view.
>
> Remember to:
>
> - write an **article**
> - use language to **argue**. *(24 marks)*

....

....

....

....

....

....

....

....

....

Don't use these language devices as a tick list in the exam, aiming to include one of each in both of your answers. **Do** look for opportunities where they will add to the impact of your ideas.

Language for effect 2

1 Look at the extracts from students' writing below. Some are taken from a piece of descriptive writing, some from a piece of argument writing. Connect the rhetorical device to the extract in which it is used.

- direct address
- pattern of three
- alliteration
- hyperbole

A For about the hundredth time that day, my sister started sobbing.

B How would you feel if it were your beloved dog or cat being treated in this way?

C The city stretched before me, dark, dangerous and disturbing.

D This is an appalling waste of money. We might as well be setting light to wads of ten pound notes and laughing as we do it.

E We must act intelligently, decisively and immediately.

F Don't just sit there! Get off the sofa and do something.

2 Now look at the exam-style question below. Write **up to four** short extracts from your answer, using **one or more** of these language techniques in **each**.

> **5** Write an **article** for your school or college website **describing** a time when you regretted something you had done, or a decision you had made.
>
> Remember to:
> - write an **article**
> - use language to **describe**. *(16 marks)*

....

....

....

....

....

....

....

....

....

....

....

Don't use these language devices as a tick list in the exam, aiming to include one of each in both of your answers. **Do** look for opportunities where they will add to the impact of your ideas.

Had a go ☐ Nearly there ☐ Nailed it! ☐

Language for effect 3

1 Look at the examples of figurative language used in the sentences below. The writers have used similes, metaphors and personification to give their writing impact. But which sentence uses which technique? Circle the correct answer.

A The wind sang in the trees and the branches waved. — simile / metaphor / personification

B The school has a challenging task ahead – an Everest to be climbed. — simile / metaphor / personification

C She smiled like a tiger, licking its lips at the sight of a lost child. — simile / metaphor / personification

D Waiting for the exams to begin is like waiting on death row. — simile / metaphor / personification

E Homework is a ball and chain around every students' ankle. — simile / metaphor / personification

F It's at that moment that your completely empty revision timetable creeps up behind you, taps you on the shoulder and asks if it could 'have a word'. — simile / metaphor / personification

2 Now look at the exam-style question below. Write **up to four** short extracts from your answer, using **one** of these language techniques in **each**.

> **6** Write an **article** for your school or college website **persuading** students to help make their school or college a better, cleaner, more inviting place to be.
>
> Remember to:
> - write an **article**
> - use language to **persuade**. *(24 marks)*

....

....

....

....

....

....

....

....

- **Don't** try to use one simile, one metaphor and one personification in both of your answers.
- **Do** look for opportunities where they will add impact to your ideas.
- **Do** avoid clichés and be original.

Putting it into practice

Answer the exam-style question below, focusing in particular on language for effect and language devices.

5 'Many people are nervous of trying new things: new food, new activities, new places.' Write an **article** for a newspaper in which you **describe** a time when you tried something new.

Remember to:

- write an **article**
- use language to **describe**.

Try to write approximately one side of your answer booklet. *(16 marks)*

When you tackle any writing question in the exam, remember to:

- be sure about the audience, purpose, form and topic for your writing
- spend 3–5 minutes gathering ideas
- organise and sequence your ideas
- select language and use language devices for effect in your writing.

Remember: You will have more space than this to answer the question in the exam. Use your own paper to finish your answer to the question above.

Had a go ☐ Nearly there ☐ Nailed it! ☐

Sentence variety 1

Guided

1 Look at the sentences below and identify the sentence type. Are they a:

- a simple sentence
- a compound sentence
- a complex sentence
- a minor sentence?

For each one, write a sentence explaining how you know which sentence type it is.

(a) We must act now because soon it may be too late. This is a .... sentence because ....

(b) Surely not. This is a .... sentence because ....
....

(c) I hurried but I was too late. This is a .... sentence because ....
....

(d) The time has come. This is a .... sentence because ....
....

Now look at the exam-style question below, then answer Questions 2 and 3.

> 6 'Sportsmen and women set an extremely bad example. They are liars, cheaters and fakers.'
> Write an **article** for a magazine of your choice, **arguing** for or against this view.
> Remember to:
> - write an **article**
> - use language to **argue**. *(24 marks)*

2 Look at the extract from one student's answer to the above exam-style question. It is entirely written in short simple sentences. Rewrite the extract, aiming to use a variety of all four different sentence types.

> Professional footballers are possibly the worst 'fakers'. With just one tap from another player they fall over. Sometimes they dive to the ground. Occasionally they fly. They always start screaming. It shows they are seriously injured. They say it was a foul. They demand a free kick. It is ridiculous.

3 Write your own short paragraph in response to the above exam-style question, aiming to use a variety of all four different sentence types.

....
....
....
....
....
....
....

Sentence variety 2

Look at the exam-style question below, then answer Questions 1 and 2.

> **5** A newspaper is inviting entries for a writing competition. The topic is 'City life or country life?' Write your **entry, explaining** why you would rather live in a city or in the countryside.
>
> Remember to:
> - write a **competition entry**
> - use language to **explain**. *(16 marks)*

Guided

1 Write a sentence that you could use in your answer to the above exam-style question, beginning with:

(a) a pronoun (e.g. I, he, she, they): I grew up in a tiny village in the middle of nowhere.

(b) an article (e.g. a, an, the): ....

(c) a preposition (e.g. above, behind, between): ....

(d) an -ing word (or present participle) (e.g. running, hurrying, crawling): ....

(e) an adjective (e.g. slow, quiet, violent): ....

(f) an adverb (e.g. alarmingly, painfully, happily): ....

(g) a connective (subordinating clause + main clause) (e.g. if, although, because): ....

2 Now write a paragraph in response to the above exam-style question. Aim to use:
- all seven different types of sentence opener in your writing
- a different word to start each of your sentences.

....

Had a go ☐ Nearly there ☐ Nailed it! ☐

Sentences for effect

Guided **1** Look at the sentences below. What effect is this series of short sentences intended to have on the reader?

> It was too late. She had seen me. I tried to smile. She snarled. I backed away. She came closer.

The short sentences are intended to create a feeling of ....

....

....

Guided **2** You can use longer sentences to convey a lot of information to the reader – and for effect. What effect is the longer sentence below intended to have on the reader?

> That moment seemed to last forever as her eyes narrowed and burned with anger, her hands clenched into heavy fists, her breath hissed like a steam train and, slowly, ever so slowly, her mouth opened and she whispered just one word.

This longer sentence is intended to create a feeling of ....

....

....

Guided **3** Look at the sentences below. What effect is the long sentence followed by the short sentence intended to have on the reader?

> The ladder tipped over, the paint pot went flying, the paint exploded over her sofa, the paint pot hit her treasured vase, and the vase smashed into dust. I froze.

The effect of the long sentence is ....

....

The effect of the short sentence is ....

....

4 Now write the opening two or three sentences of your own response to the exam-style question below. Aim to include a:

- longer sentence to suggest a slow build up of tension
- series of short sentences to create fast-paced tension
- long sentence followed by a short sentence for dramatic impact.

> **5** Write an **article** for a magazine of your choice, **describing** 'My most embarrassing moment'.
> Remember to:
> - write an **article**
> - use language to **describe**. *(16 marks)*

....

....

Putting it into practice

Answer the exam-style question below, focusing in particular on sentence variety.

5 'Everyone should try to make a difference by helping others.' Write an **article** for your local paper in which you **explain** how and why you have helped someone.

Remember to:

- write an **article**
- use language to **explain**.

Try to write approximately one page in your answer booklet. *(16 marks)*

When you tackle any writing question in the exam, remember to:

- use a range of sentence types
- begin your sentences in a range of different ways
- structure your sentences for effect.

Remember: You will have more space than this to answer the question in the exam. Use your own paper to finish your answer to the question above.

Had a go ☐ Nearly there ☐ Nailed it! ☐

Full stops, question marks and exclamation marks

1 When should you use a full stop? ....

2 When should you use a question mark? ....

3 When should you use an exclamation mark? ....

4 Look at the sentences below. Tick the two sentences that are punctuated correctly. Cross the one that is not.

A I knew that what she had done was wrong, I had to persuade her to do something about it.

B I knew that what she had done was wrong. I had to persuade her to do something about it.

C I knew that what she had done was wrong and I had to persuade her to do something about it.

Now write a sentence explaining your decision. ....

....

5 Look at this student's writing. Correct all the full stop, question mark and exclamation mark errors you can find.

A Change of Heart!!

I braced myself for a confrontation, she was looking at me like she knew I had something to say and she didn't want to hear it. My heart began to race and a strange throbbing pain pulsed in my forehead. How could I say it. How could I tell her what I was thinking without upsetting her.

She knew something was coming, tears were welling up in her dark brown eyes and her bottom lip was starting to quiver. I didn't feel much better than she did, my stomach was churning and I could feel my legs shaking. I tried to speak, my mouth felt like sandpaper, it was dry and rough and I couldn't form the words.

You do not use a comma to join two pieces of information in a sentence. Use a full stop to separate them, or a connective to join them. So check every time you use a comma: should it be a comma or a full stop?

Commas

1 Look at the sentences below. Some have used commas correctly. Some have not. Tick the correct sentences and cross the incorrect ones.

Commas in lists

☐ **A** They can comfort us in a crisis, help out when we're in trouble make us laugh or make us cry.

☐ **B** It doesn't matter whether they're tall, short, thin, fat, heart-stoppingly attractive or mirror-crackingly ugly.

☐ **C** She was loud, angry, obnoxious and painfully honest.

Commas in complex sentences with subordinating clauses

☐ **D** Whether we like it or not, friends can hurt as well as help us.

☐ **E** Friends can hurt as well as help us whether we like it or not.

☐ **F** Although I had known her since primary school we never spoke again.

Commas in complex sentences with relative clauses

☐ **G** The problem which we may not want to face, is that friends can sometimes let us down.

☐ **H** A friend who I will not name once told me all my worst faults.

☐ **I** Her house, which I only ever visited once, was enormous.

2 Look again at all the sentences in Question 1. Correct any that you marked as incorrect.

3 Now write **three to five** sentences in response to the exam-style question below, using commas correctly to separate:

- items in a list
- a main and subordinating clause
- a main and relative clause.

> 5 Write an **article** for your college website entitled 'The Perfect Friend'. **Explain** what you think makes the perfect friend and why.
>
> Remember to:
> - write an **article**
> - use language to **explain**. *(16 marks)*

....

....

....

....

....

....

....

....

....

....

....

Had a go ☐ Nearly there ☐ Nailed it! ☐

Apostrophes and speech punctuation

1 Look at the sentences below. Some have used apostrophes correctly. Some have not. Tick the correct sentences and cross the incorrect ones.

Apostrophes in contractions

☐ **A** I do'nt see her very often.

☐ **B** I can't believe how things turned out.

☐ **C** She wouldnt answer the phone.

Apostrophes of possession

☐ **D** My teachers' face was a picture.

☐ **E** The schools reaction was incredible.

☐ **F** The boys' faces all lit up.

Speech punctuation

☐ **G** 'I don't believe it!' she shouted.

☐ **H** 'Never mind.'

☐ **I** 'Come over here.' he whispered.

2 Look again at all the sentences in Question 1. Correct any that you marked as incorrect.

Guided 3 Now write a conversation between two friends in which they discuss a boy whose behaviour has resulted in a several teachers ringing his parents. Aim to use apostrophes and speech marks correctly.

'Hey,' she called. 'Come over here.'

'What do you want?' I asked. ....

....

....

....

....

....

....

....

....

Remember:

- Apostrophes in contractions are used to replace **missing letters**.
- Apostrophes of possession are always placed **at the end of the noun** whether it's plural (teachers') or singular (teacher's).
- In dialogue, there is always a punctuation mark **before** the closing speech marks.

Colons, semi-colons, dashes, brackets and ellipses

Colons and semi-colons

1 Look at the sentences below. How could you alter or add to the punctuation, using a colon or a semi-colon?

A There is only one thing you can do to improve your grades. Revise.

B Teacher's can help. They can give revision tips and answer any questions you have about the exam.

C Revision isn't easy. It takes time and willpower.

D Exams are the problem. Revision is the solution.

You can use a semi-colon to link two connected ideas instead of using a connective. You can use a colon to introduce:
- a list
- an example
- an explanation.

Dashes and brackets

2 Look at the sentences below. Some have used dashes and brackets correctly. Some have not. Tick the correct sentences and cross the incorrect ones.

☐ **A** My revision – which mainly involves staring into space – began this morning.

☐ **B** A short break (or sometimes a long break) helps clear your mind and recharge your battery.

☐ **C** My bedroom walls are covered in scribbled revision notes and key points (not a pretty sight.

☐ **D** Sometimes I wonder why I bother – and then I remember.

3 Look again at all the sentences in Question 3. Correct any that you marked as incorrect.

4 Now write **three to five** sentences in response to the exam-style question below.

Try to use:
- a colon and a semi-colon
- dashes, brackets and ellipses.

5 You have been asked to write an **article** for your school or college website entitled 'Revising for beginners'. Write your article, **describing** your experience of GCSE revision.

Remember to:
- write an **article**
- use language to **describe**. *(16 marks)*

....

....

....

....

....

....

....

Had a go ☐ Nearly there ☐ Nailed it! ☐

Putting it into practice

Answer the exam-style question below, focusing in particular on punctuation.

5 Your local newspaper is inviting students to write an **article**. The topic is 'I'll never forget when …'. Write your article, **describing** an unforgettable experience.

Remember to:

- write an **article**
- use language to **describe**.

Try to write approximately one page in your answer booklet. *(16 marks)*

When you tackle any writing question in the exam, remember to:

- use a range of punctuation, including advanced punctuation such as colons and semi-colons
- save time after you have finished writing to check the accuracy of your punctuation.

Remember: You will have more space than this to answer the question in the exam. Use your own paper to finish your answer to the question above.

Common spelling errors 1

Some of the most common spelling errors in students' writing are a result of confusing:

- would of and would have
- should of and should have
- could of and could have
- our and are
- their, there, and they're
- affect and effect
- words ending in ley and ely
- its and it's

1 Identify and correct any spelling errors in these sentences.

A They went all the way back to there house.

B It would of been absolutley unbelievable –if I hadn't seen it with my own eyes.

C One affect of this issue is extremley concerning.

D Their first problem was how to get the students interested.

E Their our three reasons for this.

F There refusing to do anything about it.

G The school offered it's help immediately.

H We felt that students should definitley of been involved.

I Its not only the teachers who our effected by this situation.

J We were forced to reconsider are plan.

K It could not of been achieved without there help.

L Many students felt it had affected them negativley.

M Its not the first time this has happened.

- There are very few words ending in **ley**.
- **Would of**, **could of** and **should of** are **always** incorrect.

Had a go ☐ Nearly there ☐ Nailed it! ☐

Common spelling errors 2

Some of the most common spelling errors in students' writing are a result of confusing:

your and you're

two, too and to

we're, were, where and wear

of and off

whose and who's

passed and past

1 Identify and correct any spelling errors in these sentences:

A He did not know were he was going or who's idea it was.

B To many people make the same mistake.

C The time for worrying has past.

D This has taken some of the pressure of us.

E Your never sure whether you're doing enough to help.

F Whose going to complain about that?

G We where the first people there but still they ignored us.

H They walked passed us as though we wear invisible.

I They went too far, taking it too an extreme.

J How can we tell who's to blame?

K It can be difficult to know when your in the wrong.

L Support for the idea soon began to fall of.

M We simply don't know whose argument to believe and whether were expected to agree or not.

Remember:
A lot is two words. '**Alot** of people make this mistake' is wrong, but '**A lot** of people make this mistake' is correct.

Common spelling errors 3

1 Look carefully at the words below. In each row, one is spelt correctly and the others are spelt incorrectly. Tick the correct spelling, and cross the incorrect spelling or spellings.

arguement	argument	argumant
dificult	difficult	diffacult
disappoint	dissappoint	disapoint
disappear	dissappear	disapear
embarasing	embarassing	embarrassing
possesion	possession	posession
beggining	begining	beginning
recomend	recommend	reccomend
occassionaly	ocasionally	occasionally
definately	definitely	definitley
separately	seperately	seperatley
conscious	conshus	concsous
conshence	conscience	concsience
experiance	experance	experience
indapendance	independence	independance
beleive	believe	beleve
weird	wierd	weerd
business	busness	buisness
rythm	rhytm	rhythm
decision	desicion	desision
greatfull	grateful	greatful

2 Now check your answers on page 113. Use the space below to learn and practise any spellings you are not sure about.

Had a go ☐ Nearly there ☐ Nailed it! ☐

Proofreading

1 Look at the extract from one student's writing below. Read it carefully, looking for any:
- spelling errors
- punctuation errors
- grammatical errors – e.g. misused, repeated or missing words.

Circle and correct all the errors you can find.

> Scotland is the most amazing place Ive ever visited, even though it took ten hours to drive there it was worth it the moment i saw were we were staying. Huge blue lochs, rolling green hills, miles and miles of pine forest. They even looked beautiful driving passed them in a car.
>
> On the first day we took the dogs for a long walk through a forest, it was the quitest place Ive ever been. Even with my brother their, all you could hear was the sound of leafs rustling in the breeze, the birds singing and you're heart beating.
>
> Are hotel was great, the scottish people are so frendly. I would definitley stay there again.

2 Look back at three or four pieces of writing you have completed recently. How many errors can you find? In the table below, note down words which you have misspelled and the **kinds** of punctuation and grammatical errors you have made.

Spelling errors	Punctuation errors	Grammatical errors

Train your proofreading brain to look out for the kinds of punctuation and grammatical errors you are prone to making. When the alarm rings, **stop!** Double check and correct any mistakes.

3 Use the space below to practise and learn all the spellings you have noted in the table.

Putting it into practice

Answer the exam-style question below, focusing in particular on proofreading your answer.

6 'Far too much pressure is placed on young people – pressure from adults, from school and from the media.' Write an **article** for your school or college website, **arguing** for or against this view.

Remember to:

- write an **article**
- use language to **argue**.

Try to write approximately two sides of your answer booklet. *(24 marks)*

When you tackle any writing question in the exam, remember to:

- save time after you have finished writing to check the accuracy of your writing
- look out for the spelling, punctuation and grammatical errors which you know you often make.

Remember: You will have more space than this to answer the question in the exam. Use your own paper to finish your answer to the question above.

Foundation practice paper

This Practice Exam Paper has been written to help you practise what you have learned and may not be representative of a real exam paper.

You will be given more space than this in the exam, so complete your answers on extra paper.

Sources 1, 2 and 3 are provided at the back of this paper.

English/English Language (exam)

Unit 1 Understanding and producing non-fiction texts

Time allowed

- 2 hours and 15 minutes

Section A: Reading

Answer **all** questions in this section.

You are advised to spend about one hour on this section.

Read **Source 1**, the newspaper article *Father who lost arm in work accident has bionic 'Terminator hand'* and answer the questions below.

1 **(a)** List **four** things which Nigel Ackland is now able to do with his 'bionic hand'. *(4 marks)*

1 ....

....

2 ....

....

3 ....

....

4 ....

....

(b) How does Nigel feel about his new 'bionic hand'? *(4 marks)*

....

....

....

....

....

....

....

....

....

8

Now read **Source 2**, the *Think U Know* webpage.

2 Explain the advice which the webpage gives about social networking sites.

Remember to:
- show your understanding by explaining in your own words
- support your ideas using the text.

(8 marks)

8

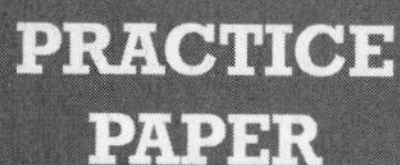

Now read **Source 3**, the webpage article called *Real Lives: Teenage Cancer*.

3 How does the writer use **language features** to **inform** the reader and **describe** his experiences?

Remember to:

- give some examples of language features to inform
- give some examples of language features to describe
- explain the effects.

(12 marks)

12

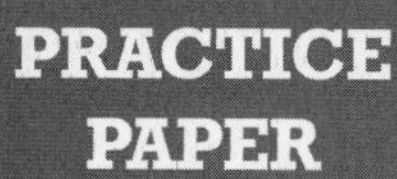

4 Look again at **Source 1** and **Source 2** and compare the way that both texts use **presentational features** for effect.

Remember to:

- write about the way the sources are **presented**
- explain the **effect** of the presentational features
- compare the way they **look**. *(12 marks)*

12

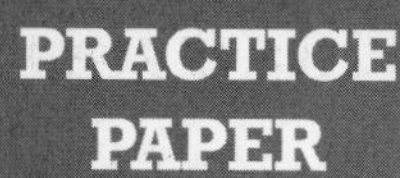

Section B: Writing

Answer **both** questions in this section.

You are advised to spend about one hour on this section.

You are advised to spend about 25 minutes on question 5.

You are advised to spend about 35 minutes on question 6.

---

5 Write an **article** for your school or college website, **describing** a time when you faced a challenge and overcame it.

Remember to:
- write an **article**
- use language to **describe**.

Try to write approximately one side of your answer booklet. *(16 marks)*

16

Turn over ▸

PRACTICE
PAPER

6 A television company has written to the head of your school or college. They want to spend six weeks at your school or college filming a reality television series about the teachers and students.

Write a **letter persuading** your head teacher either to allow the filming or to refuse it.

Remember to:

- write a **letter**
- use language to **persuade**.

Try to write approximately two sides of your answer booklet. *(24 marks)*

Turn over ▸

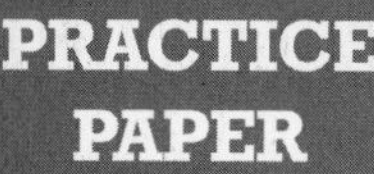

Turn over ▸

Source 1

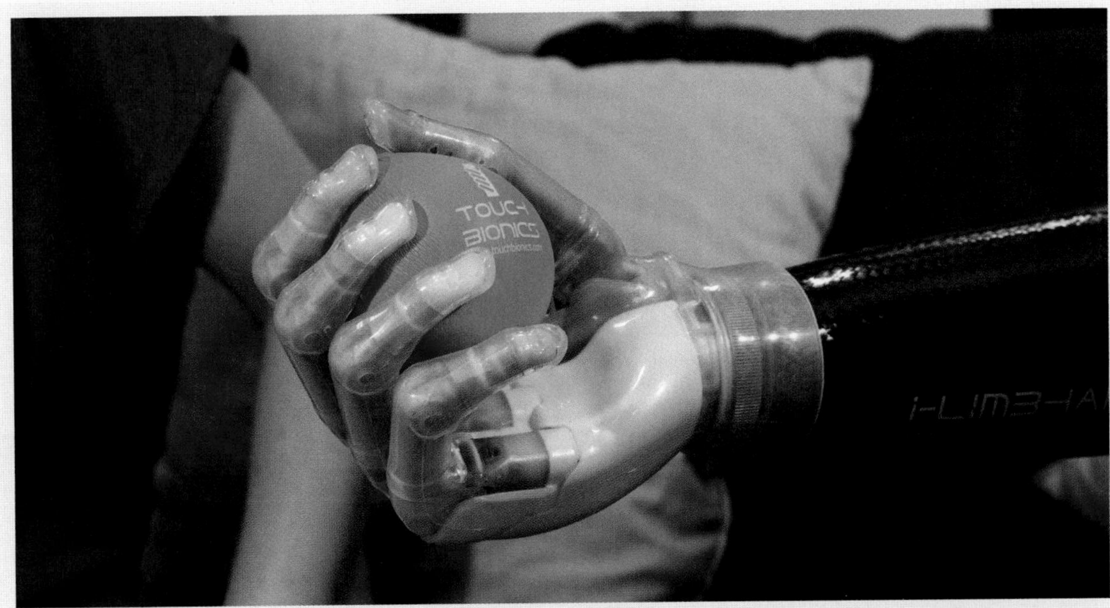

Father who lost arm in work accident has bionic 'Terminator hand'

A father who lost his arm in an accident six years ago has been given a new lease of life by a high-tech bionic hand which is so precise he can type again.

Nigel Ackland, 53, has been fitted with the Terminator-like carbon fibre mechanical hand which he can control with movements in his upper arm. Incredibly, the robotic arm is so sensitive it means the dad-of-one Nigel can touch type on a computer keyboard, peel vegetables, and even dress himself for the first time in six years.

He said: 'When you lose a part of you it can take you into quite a dark place. Prior to this I used prosthetic limbs provided by the NHS which were horrible. I used a hook which didn't resemble a hand at all.

'Things like tying a shoelace and chopping a vegetable are now much easier. I am slowly becoming more at one with it, the fingers even move when I yawn and stretch, but it will never be the same as having my own hand.'

Nigel was approached by Leeds-based prosthetics company, RSLSteeper, in May this year and asked if he would like to trial their latest hand – the most high-tech available in the world.

While the hand has changed his life, Nigel says it still has limitations and the keen musician has not been able to start playing the piano and saxophone again.

Nigel added: 'When you first lose a limb it can take a massive blow to your confidence. People in the street don't really know how to react to the fact that you have no arm and as a result you can be left feeling exceptionally withdrawn.

'With the Terminator arm people will come up and ask you about it. It is almost like it is science fiction for them, which is amazing. I don't really like people feeling sorry for me or shying away from me, so for that not to be happening is life-changing.

'Since I started the trial it has made a massive difference to my day-to-day life and my health as well. It is like being your old-self, with a very cool piece of machinery helping you.'

The total cost of making the arm, the programming and consultation is estimated at around £25,000.

Source 2

THINK U KNOW
HOW TO HAVE FUN
HOW TO STAY IN CONTROL
HOW TO REPORT

- Cyberbullying
- Mobiles
- Chat rooms
- Gaming
- Social networking
- Viruses
- Sexting

What information you give out ...

Be careful what information you give out on your profile. Remember that you don't know who your friend's friends are … or your friend's friends' friends! And you don't know what they'll do with your picture or your phone number if you give it out by mistake. Once your picture is out there, it's out there forever and you won't be able to get it back.

Be aware that information on your profile could potentially be viewed by anyone. So if you wouldn't be comfortable printing it off and handing it out on the street, maybe it shouldn't be on your profile.

Use a nickname or your initials instead of your name – you don't want just anyone knowing who you are. Consider changing your photo to a cool graphic or picture of your favourite band, that way strangers won't have access to a picture of you. It's not a great idea to post where you're going on your profile or twitter or where you live. Think through if you'd want everyone who can view the post to turn up at any time!

Who to chat to ...

Think through who you want to chat to and how many of your personal thoughts you want anyone to view. Sometimes, it can seem a good idea to share what you got up to with your boyfriend last night, or the argument you had with your best mate; but as you're writing – remember that information could be public forever! It is tempting to share loads of stuff on your profile, especially since you're often typing from the comfort of your own home. But remember, the internet is a public space. Test yourself by asking 'Would I want my teacher/Mum/Dad/stranger on the train to see this?!' If the answer's no … don't post it!

Source 3

Real Lives: Teenage Cancer

How does it feel to find that your future is under threat while you're still growing up? Here Tom Marton shares his story

On New Year's Day 2013 I'm going to put a message on my Facebook page saying something very rude that means: 2012 was bad. Very, very bad. The worst year of my life; the worst year I can possibly imagine.

The weird thing is that just a few weeks before I was diagnosed, I remember thinking: is this what life is? Is it things carrying on the same way, am I just going to go to school each day, then go to work each day, getting older, and then eventually die? Does anything actually happen?

And then something did. It started as a headache, with slight double vision. The doctor thought it was a migraine. But it didn't go away, so I had an MRI scan and they told my mum it was a brain tumour (I was too ill to even know what was going on by that stage.) Mum and Dad are divorced, so Mum had to phone Dad to tell him. She was so upset, he thought I was dead.

The tumour was in the centre of my brain, and it was causing a massive pressure build-up, so the next day I was in surgery for four hours while they tried to drain it. After that there were weeks of chemotherapy, including one stage where I was given high-dose drugs which killed off my immune system. It was all scary stuff.

And then came the big one – a 14-hour operation to remove the tumour. I knew there were risks but I didn't want to know too much: my attitude is that it's best to concentrate on doing what you can to make things go right. I see my illness as an unexpected river I've got to cross on my life's journey. It's a daunting river and it's very difficult getting across it, but all I can do is build my bridge, and when things are tough I keep on building it, brick by brick.

Many kids of my age are all into their friends – and my friends have been important. But when something like this happens to you, you realise what family means: my family have been fantastic – my parents, my brother, my half-brother, my step-brother and sister. When my hair fell out, my brother and my step-brother both shaved their heads in solidarity: that meant a lot to me.

Two weeks after the surgery I came home, and I'm now going to Leeds each weekday for radiotherapy – it's a three-hour round trip plus half an hour of radiotherapy. That's going to carry on for the next six weeks or so, after which we'll see what they say.

Cancer has messed up my life, there's no getting round it. People say I'm inspiring and strong – I hate that. I'm no superhero, just a boy who wants to stay alive, doing what the doctors and nurses tell him in the hope of one day getting his life back.

Answers

SECTION A : READING

1. Questions 1 and 2

1 **(a)** 1a; a
(b) 1b; a
(c) 2; b

2. Questions 3 and 4

1 **(a)** 3; a; b
(b) 4; b

3. Planning your time in the exam

1 15 minutes
2 6 minutes
3 6 minutes
4 12 minutes
5 18 minutes
6 18 minutes
7 All of them

4. Reading the questions

1 **(a)** Source 2
(b) reasons / persuade / reader / donate / money
(c) 8
(e) 12 minutes

2 **Q1 (b)**
- Source 1
- learn / people of Birmingham / hopes for the future
- 4 marks
- 6 minutes

Q3:
- Source 3
- use language features
- 12 marks
- 18 minutes

Q4:
- Source 3 and Source 1 or Source 2
- compare / presentational features / effect
- 12 marks
- 18 minutes

5. Approaching the exam paper

1 **Q1 (a):** Source 1; list four things, city of Birmingham; 4 marks.
Q1 (b): Source 1; people of Birmingham, hopes for the future; 4 marks.
Q2: Source 2; persuade; donate money; 8 marks.
Q3: Source 3; language features, inform, describe, effects; 12 marks.
Q4: Source 3 and either Source 1 or 2; compare way, presentational features for effect; 12 marks.

2 15 minutes:
- read questions
- skim read source texts
- read source texts carefully
- read questions, read texts again, and highlight relevant information.

6 minutes: answer Q1 (a)
6 minutes: answer Q1 (b)
12 minutes: answer Q2
18 minutes: answer Q3
18 minutes: answer Q4

6. Skimming for the main idea

1 The Day of the Dead is when people in Mexico and other places celebrate the lives of their dead relatives.

2 The Day of the Dead is when people in Mexico and other places celebrate the lives of their dead relatives by dressing up, eating in graveyards and decorating the graves.

7. Annotating the sources

1 **B**, **C**, **D** and **E** all focus on the consequences of fame.
A states a fact that is not directly relevant to the question.

2

> **'They ask your wife to take the photo, which is a bit rude**,' Wiggins says of some well-wishers. 'And after a while **that becomes tiresome**, especially when you're having a pizza with your children, or **you have to have a photo with somebody else's kids while yours stand to the side**.'
> Wiggins, 32, says **he finds it particularly hard that his celebrity status takes any attention from his wife**, who is herself British champion. He says: 'Nobody ever asks her how she is. It's always, "How's Brad doing?" Nobody ever says to her, "How are you doing, Cath? How are you handling it all?" **It's very difficult for her**.'
> Earlier in his career, in a lull following his three-medal haul from the 2004 Olympics, **Wiggins had a period in which he drank heavily**. In the interview he describes a period where he would arrive at his local pub when it opened, often staying to drink 12 pints of beer. 'I was just bored and didn't know what to do.' The nine-month binge caused the usually beanpole-framed cyclist to put on significant weight: 'I got quite big. I wasn't huge. I was probably 83 kilos.'
> It ended when his son, Ben, was born: 'We had a baby. So then it was a case of, well, I've got to earn some money and the responsibility takes over.'
> A lack of money had been one of the post-Olympic depressions Wiggins faced. He says: 'It got me down. **You think if you win the Olympics, you'll become a millionaire overnight. But I was still scraping the barrel**, looking down the back of the settee for pound coins to buy a pint of milk.'

8. Selecting information

1 All of these could be relevant: they suggest an uncomfortable flight on a small and very old aircraft in a remote location.

2

> 'Clear prop!' The engine splutters into life. Soon we are cantering along, gathering speed and generously throwing up dust for all and sundry. But there is no all, and there is no sundry, just our guide sitting nonchalantly astride the bonnet of his 4×4 to wave off another batch of **wilderness seekers**. Some distance behind him, **two fire buckets hang, lifeless, from a T-shaped frame next to the lavatory, which has a pointed roof made from sticks. That's it. There is no control tower, no emergency services – just miles and miles of nothingness**.
> We are heading to our camp, **a comfortable oasis of calm** beside the river. By air it is a relatively straightforward journey; back in the 4×4, it would involve a huge amount of **bumping, churning and sliding** over **desert rock and sand** to get there.
> The altimeter needle continues to turn as the views widen; detail is lost as patterns emerge, **nature's patterns**, completely **devoid of influence from man's busying hand**. At cruising height, the desert gives way to mountains, carved and fissured rock massifs.
> **Dry rivers trace steep-sided valleys**, where twin lines of hardy bushes mark the boundaries of an **infrequent flow of water**. But within this seeming barrenness is **life**.
> We have witnessed the **regal oryx** with his lethal horns, striding the plains and scampering up mountain slopes; the **desert-adapted rhino** with his grumpy ways, his lumbering, trundling gait. The list goes on; life goes on, resilient, changing.
> Then the pilot smiles and offers us a spherical bag. 'We're landing soon to refuel – **anyone for biltong**?'

9. Purpose and audience

1 Purpose: inform
Audience: adults / older teenagers

2 Purpose: persuade
Audience: teenagers / children

3 Purpose: describe
Audience: adults

10/11. Putting it into practice

1 Possible answers include:
- designed by British Special Forces
- an extreme test of strength and stamina
- nearly 9000 people took part in 2012
- includes up to 30 different obstacles
- £90 to enter
- takes an average of four hours to complete
- only four out of five are expected to finish the course
- more than half a million people have completed the course since 2009.

12. The writer's viewpoint

1 People show their emotions too readily and won't be able to cope when something really serious happens to them.

13. Fact, opinion and expert evidence

1 **(a)** **A** is a fact.
(b) **C** is an opinion.
(c) **B** is expert evidence.

2 GM crops were intended to resist weeds and pests but it seems they do not.

3 **Fact:** The weight of chemicals used has increased by 183 million kilos since 1996; this statistic supports the overall argument, the huge number surprising and shocking the reader.
Opinion: The findings dramatically undermine the case for adopting GM crops; the word 'dramatically' emphasising the writer's viewpoint and directing the reader's response to the facts.
Expert evidence: 'Professor Charles Benbrook said ...'; the professor's opinion further supports the writer's viewpoint, further validating it with his expertise and position as university professor.

14. Inference

1 numbers are increasing; out of control.

2 an increasingly dangerous threat ...

3 Key points to make: the dangerous fox cub is actually a terminally ill adult; dogs are more dangerous than foxes.

15. Point-Evidence-Explain

1 **Evidence A** and **B** are more effective because it allows for comment on the writer's language choice.
Evidence C does not prove the point.

2/3 **Explain B and C** are more effective as they focuses more closely on the language used and its effect on the reader.

16/17. Putting it into practice

1 **Key points:** Ranulph Fiennes is in some ways typical of an older person, as he cannot work his phone; but he is adventurous and incredibly tough.

18. Selecting evidence

1/2 **A** Not relevant to the question.
B Suggests her relationship with her father was difficult, emphasised by repetition.
C Not relevant to the question.
D Emphasises their difficult relationship.
E Suggests she is desperate to win the affection of her emotionally distant father.
Note the extended metaphor that runs throughout the extract: chasing after her father on the bike reflects their emotional relationship.

19. Embedding quotations

1 [He realises he must] 'tough it out' and 'maintain my cool' to stop himself from 'freaking out'.

2 Baumgartner enjoyed the freedom just before the jump and was relieved when his parachute opened.

3 For example:
- sweetest moment
- my feet outside the capsule
- completely released
- five years
- unique
- outstanding
- I'm still alive!

4 For example:
Baumgartner's 'sweetest moment' was when his feet were 'outside the capsule' and he could enjoy the freedom of being 'completely released'. He describes this feeling as 'unique' and 'outstanding'. Another great moment was when he realised during the jump that he was 'still alive!'.

20. Develop your explanations

1 **B**, **C**, **D** and **E** are the most relevant and effective comments.
A does not fully answer the question.

2 A suggested order would be B, C, E and D.

3 Key points:
- emotive language ('shocked and winded') focuses on the physical and emotional effects
- use of statistics ('1000 lb beast') emphasises the danger of the situation
- 'possessed' suggests almost supernatural, emphasising how dangerous and unpredictable the animal is.

21. Word classes

1 For example:
noun – handbags
verb – lose
adjective – safe
adverb – exactly.

2 Emphasises the number of times, and the variety of places in which, the writer has lost her handbag.

3 For example: 'diving' suggests the height, steepness and exhilaration of the journey.

4 'blue sky' and 'mountain tops clear' paint the scene vividly but briefly.

22/23. Putting it into practice

1 Possible key points:
- He finds it strange to be mobbed by fans in Belgium when no one in London takes any notice of him.
- He worked hard to become successful.
- He became a rapper by accident.
- He chose Belgium because he thought there would be less competition for fame and success.
- He enjoys fame but likes to be anonymous in his home town.

24. Connotations

1 'miracles' suggests religion, magic
'addiction' suggests obsession, drugs, reliance

2 For example:
The word 'addiction' has connotations of reliance and drug use. This suggests that smartphone users cannot live without, or give up, their phones.

3 For example:
- shattering – suggests violent destruction which cannot be repaired
- chirping – suggests bird song, pointless chattering
- virtuoso – suggests enormous and impressive skill.

25. Rhetorical devices 1

1 Alliteration – furry friends
Rhetorical question – Why the hell not?
Repetition – Large ones, small **ones**. Sucked **ones**, chewed **ones**.
Lists – bears, geese, rabbits ...
Emotive language – victims of a firing squad.
A short sentence – Nameless ones.

26. Rhetorical devices 2

1 For example:
Rhetorical question – Or are we?
Repetition – **never** know the love of a human being, **never** sit on a sofa ...
Lists – never know the love of a human being, never sit on a sofa ...
Emotive language – enslaved.
Contrast – picturesque / grotesque.
Pattern of three – poor rearing, lack of socialisation and lack of health tests.

27. Figurative language

1 'shine' suggests:
- intelligence (connotations of brightness)
- value (connotations of gold, silver, etc.)

2 For example: 'buckets of cold water' suggests:
- a shock
- extinguishing a fire, suggesting the extinguishing of enthusiasm.

3 'like a plant needs water' suggests that encouragement is essential to life and to growth, and allows children to 'flower' – that is, reach their full potential.

28/29. Putting it into practice

1 Points could include:

Describe
- contrast of 'smiling from ear to ear' with announcement of tattoo
- descriptive examples of son's 'hard man act' (e.g. 'iron muscles', 'shaved head')
- emotive language to describe how upset the mother is ('His lovely shoulder')
- a metaphor – 'pit of black nothingness' to describe awkward silence.

Explain
- uses facts to explain her upset ('for three days, I can't speak to my son')
- uses metaphor to explain her anger ('white-hot words')
- explains her feelings, imagining herself as 'a bitter old woman'
- rhetorical question helps to explain her confusion by showing her unsure about her feelings ('Why would you want to, anyway?').

30. Identifying sentence types

1 **A** simple
B complex
C compound
D minor

2 For example:
Simple – Adrian and Gillian Bayford won £148 million on the lottery.
Compound – The couple flew on easyJet to Scotland, and then travelled to Carnoustie on the east coast.
Complex – Despite the life-changing sum, the couple have said they are determined to remain grounded.
Minor – An incredible sum.

31. Commenting on sentence types

1 Short sentences create a sense of tension, suggesting the writer's fear and breathlessness.

2 These still shorter sentences create more tension, suggesting a build up of fear.

3 The writer uses several simple and short compound sentences to heighten the tension still further, suggesting he is building up to a climax.
The use of minor sentences heightens this effect, emphasising the writer's terror and regret at, what he suggests could be, the end of his life.

32. Making the best comments

1 C1, B2, E3, A4, D5.

2 Possible points:
Sentence structure – 'I felt sad and desperately lonely. But I didn't tell anyone.' Two short sentences create blunt and desperate tone.
Language choice – 'best ... most glamorous' superlatives build up the writer's expectations.
Viewpoint – irony of the writer and her friend's similar reactions to each other's Facebook pages emphasises the key point that Facebook does not always honestly reflect people's experience.
Effect on reader – rhetorical question on title invites reader to question their own honesty.

33. Comment on language and purpose: argue and persuade

1 The rhetorical question engages the reader, inviting them to consider what they would do in this situation. It implies that no one would do this. The short sentence answers the question clearly and bluntly. The effect of this is to contrast sharply with the expected response to the question, and so further engaging the reader.

2 **(a)** The writer uses emotive language – e.g. 'outraged', 'die' – to emphasise the extreme reactions and emotions which this topic can create.
(b) The writer lists a variety of dangers which pet owners are prepared to face, 'rivers, oceans, fights and fires', to suggest that there is no danger which a pet owner would not face to save the life of their much loved animal.

34. Comment on language and purpose: describe

1 **(a)** Describing using the five senses: the writer uses a wealth of sensory detail to evoke the scene for the reader – e.g. sight ('a hooded figure'), sound ('of the ocean'), touch ('soft, sandy beach').
(b) Figurative language: compares surfers to praying mantises, comparing them to insects emphasises how small and insignificant they seem in the water; 'praying' suggests an almost religious devotion to their sport.
(c) Language choice: e.g. 'hooded' and 'gliding' suggest a mysterious almost supernatural figure, engaging the reader as we try to work out who he is and what he is doing.
(d) The writer's feelings: does not feature in this extract.

35. Comment on language and purpose: inform and explain

1 The tone of the article is light-hearted and flippant. This tone is created through the writer's choice of language – e.g. 'stroppy' – and directly addressing the reader – e.g. 'your'.

2 The tone of the article becomes much more formal as it introduces the scientific study – e.g. 'beneficial', 'important social activities'. This suggests the information is valid and reliable.

3 **(a)** Statistics are used to support the article's main points – e.g. 'Girls aged between 10 and 12 are the happiest group of children' – reinforcing the validity and reliability of the information.
(b) Connectives are not extensively used to signal the article's structure.

36/37. Putting it into practice

1 Key points could include:

Describe
- describes his son's enjoyment ('lapping it up')
- sensory language describing sound ('shrieking Daleks')

Inform
- use of facts ('new home of the Doctor Who Experience in Porth Teigr Cardiff Bay')
- lists experiences at the musem (for example, 'flying the TARDIS')
- use of opinion ('a tad tame').

38. Identifying presentational devices 1

Answers could include:
Colour: Greenback ground suggests life and health, particularly combined with the cheerful bright red of the apple logo
Font: Putting your child first slogan in children's handwriting emphasises the focus of the charity on young people.
Headings: Your visit, Your care, Your life headings emphasise the range of information available on the website
Images: happy children and caring adults create a positive mood, encouraging patients' and parents' confidence
Logo: bright red colour and smiling face of the apple intended to appeal to young patients and encourage adults to donate to the charity.

39. Identifying presentational devices 2

Answers could include:
Bullet points: organise key information and statistics clearly and accessibly
Table: to organise key facts clearly and allow easy comparison of rank order
Sections/boxes: highlights key findings of the report using a coloured background
Paragraphs: breaks the information given into three easily understood sections.

40. Using P-E-E to comment on presentational devices

1 D, A, F, C, E, B.

2 Possible points – e.g. The boy is looking at the book, suggesting the scheme is effective in encouraging him to read.

41. Commenting on headlines

1 A, B, C

2 B

3 C

4 A, D

5 All

6 All

42. Image and effect

1 Answers should focus on how the chosen image supports the writer's point of view and its effect on the reader.

43. Comparing the presentation of two source texts

1 **(a)** Source 1, to persuade.
(b) Source 2, to persuade.

2/3 Source 1: the image shows a huge and shocking mound of rubbish, emphasising the need to recycle
Source 2: the image shows someone enjoying the kind of activity holiday which is available in Wales, suggesting to the reader that they will too.

44/45. Putting it into practice

1 Possible points include these.
- The logo repeats and emphasises the key point made by the images that, in many places, people have to collect water from pumps.
- The headings direct the reader and emphasise impact of these issues.
- The image of dirty water emphasises the hidden dangers of water.
- The blue heading/background reinforce idea of water.

46. Planning to compare presentation

1 Plans should be detailed, including points, evidence and explanations.

47. Answering a compare question

1 All points of comparison should be supported with evidence and explanation focusing on effect.

48/49. Putting it into practice

1 Key points could include the following.
Source 1:
- use of green draws attention to key features, e.g. logo, 'donate' button, suggests positive attitude, moving forward
- logo: shows adults physically supporting a child, reflecting the charity's work
- 6 list: emphasises the range of ways in which people can support the charity
- image: shows how people can help by donating shoes
- graphic: emphasises visually how much of a potential donation supports the charity's work.

Source 2:
- heading font suggests design/engineering
- flow diagram represents information visually and clearly the path from school to paid work
- school and work in large white font emphasise this path
- notepad/paper clips/images of engineers give real examples of people who have followed this path.

SECTION B : READING

50. Reading the questions

1 **(a)** National newspaper
(b) Adults, school / college students.

2 Describe

3 Article

4 A school day you particularly enjoyed.

5 Head teacher

6 Arguing

7 Letter

8 All students should complete at least one month's paid work experience before they leave school, for or against.

51. The questions and planning your exam time

1 25 minutes

2 35 minutes

3 **Q5:** 5 minutes to plan; about 15 minutes to write; about 3 minutes to check.
Q6: 5 minutes to plan; about 25 minutes to write; about 3 minutes to check.

52. Writing for an audience

1 The audience for A is likely to be adults and teenagers. The audience for B is likely to include students, teachers, school governors, and parents.

2 **(b)**

3 **(a)** The more formal opening sentences are appropriate for the audiences of both tasks.

53. Writing for a purpose: inform and explain

3 Answers should be written in a formal tone, using a range of supporting facts/statistics.

54. Writing for a purpose: describe

4 Answers could include description using the five senses, the writer's feelings, and figurative language.

55. Writing for a purpose: argue and persuade

1 Examples of points **for** the point of view could include: 'People spend hours on the Internet';' Like other addictive drugs, people's use increases the more they use it, becoming more and more dependent';' People denied access can suffer cravings'.
Examples of points **against** the point of view could include: 'The time people spend on the Internet shows how useful it is';'It does not cause physical harm';'Using the Internet is no different to reading a book or meeting friends, except it is onscreen'.

56. Putting it into practice

1 **Q5:** 25 minutes; **Q6:** 35 minutes.

2 **Q5:** purpose –explain; form – article; topic – the most important thing you learned at school.
Q6: audience – adults/older teenagers; form – article; topic – men and women can never be equal.

3 **Q5:** e.g. subheadings, facts/statistics, formal language.
Q6: e.g. key points, evidence, rhetorical devices, counter-argument.

57. Form: letters and emails

1

Your address
Date

Their address

Dear Mr Smith
I am writing regarding your recent letter to parents and students, dated 13 September

and hope you will consider this before making any decision.
Yours sincerely

Your signature
Your name

2 You do not need to include either addresses or the date in a formal email.

58. Form: articles

Answers will vary but students should include in their article a headline, a subheading, an opening paragraph summing up their ideas and a concluding paragraph. They may also include a quotation.

59. Form: information sheets

Answers will vary but students should include in their information sheet a title, subheadings and evidence of use of structural features such as bullet points, a table, etc.

60 Putting it into practice

1 Key features/points to include are:
- form – your address, the head's address, date, salutation and sign off all correctly laid out.
- audience – appropriately formal language
- purpose – persuasive points, supported with evidence, use of rhetorical devices and a counter-argument
- topic – clear focus on the positive **OR** negative impact of homework.

61 Planning an answer: describe

1 Plans should include details of the five senses, feelings, details to create mood or atmosphere, language for effect.

62. Planning an answer: inform or explain

1 Plans should include three sequenced points, supported with some detail, and an introduction.

63. Planning an answer: argue or persuade

1 Plans should include three sequenced points supported with evidence, a counter-argument, introduction and conclusion.

64. Beginnings

2 Introductions should feature at least one of the approaches outlined in Q1, introduce the topic and give the writer's point of view.

65. Endings

2 Conclusions should feature at least one of the approaches outlined in Q1.

66. Putting it into practice

The plan should include an introduction, some key points, supporting evidence, a counter argument and a conclusion.

67. Paragraphing

1 **Point:** When students choose …
Evidence: I chose my GCSEs …
Explain: Neither of these …

68. Using connectives

1

Adding an idea	Explaining	Illustrating	Emphasising	Comparing	Contrasting
Moreover … *Furthermore …* *In addition …* *Not only … but also*	*because* *therefore* *consequently*	*For example* *For instance* *Such as*	*In particular* *Especially* *Significantly*	*Similarly* *In the same way*	*However* *On the other hand* *… whereas …*

2 **Paragraph 1 examples:** For example …; therefore …
Paragraph 2 examples: Moreover … Significantly …; … for instance …
Paragraph 3 examples: However …

69. Putting it into practice

Answers should be paragraphed accurately and use connectives to guide the reader through the text.

70. Getting the right tone

1 Teachers, parents, students
2 Formal
3 Teenage gamers
4 Informal, perhaps using some slang.
5 Point of view
Scrap 1: A
Scrap 2: B
Formal or informal
Scrap 1: A
Scrap 2: B
Standard English or non-standard English
Scrap 1: B
Scrap 2: N

71. Synonyms

1 Students: *pupils, exam candidates, learners.*
Improve: *develop, enhance, extend.*
Learning: *achievement, attainment, skills.*
Doing: *completing, achieving, carrying out, performing.*
More: *further, a greater amount of, a larger quantity of.*
2 Embarrassed: *humiliated, ashamed, mortified.*
Upset: *concerned, worried, alarmed.*
Scream: *yell, shriek, shout.*
Moment: *occasion, time, situation.*
Annoyed: *aggravated, agitated, distressed.*

72. Choosing vocabulary for effect: describe

1 Beams of sunlight danced on my walls.
2 The original sentence is over-written. It contains far too much description. Selecting vocabulary carefully is far more effective than cramming in as much description as possible.

73. Choosing vocabulary for effect: argue and persuade

1 **(b)** Examples include:
use too many > *devour, fritter*
not have enough food > *starve*
(c) Examples include:
filled with > *dominated by, ruled by*
not like > *hate, detest*
cannot do much about it > *are powerless to change it*
2 'Roar' suggests a lion – therefore, loudness, anger, aggression, dominance.
3 'Whimper' suggests weakness.

74. Language for effect 1

1 **A** Rhetorical question
B Rhetorical question
C Contrast, list
D Contrast
E Contrast, list, repetition
F Repetition

75. Language for effect 2

1 **A** Hyperbole, alliteration
D Direct address
C Alliteration, pattern of three
D Hyperbole
E Pattern of three
F Direct address

76. Language for effect 3

1 **A** Personification
B Metaphor
C Simile
D Simile
E Metaphor
F Personification

77. Putting it into practice

Answers should feature a range of language and language devices chosen for effect.

78. Sentence variety 1

1 **(a)** Complex: two verbs, two clauses, linked with *because.*
(b) Minor: no verb.
(c) Compound: two verbs, two clauses, linked with *but.*
(d) Simple: one verb.
2 For example: *Professional footballers are possibly the worst 'fakers'. With just one tap from another player they fall over, dive to the ground or occasionally fly. They always start screaming because it shows they are seriously injured. They say it was a foul. They demand a free kick. Ridiculous.*

79. Sentence variety 2

2 Sentences should each start with a different word and a range of word classes including pronoun, article, preposition, present participle, adjective, adverb and connective.

80. Sentences for effect

1 Short sentences can be used to build fast-paced tension.
2 The longer sentence creates a slow build-up of tension
3 The long sentence emphasises the chain of events, and builds tension as the situation worsens. The short sentence brings it to an abrupt end, focusing on the narrator's horror.

81. Putting it into practice

Answers should include a range of sentence types crafted for effect, and a range of sentence openings.

82. Full stops, question marks and exclamation marks

1 At the end of a sentence.
2 At the end of a question.
3 At the end of an exclamation – but use them sparingly and only one at a time.
4 **A** Incorrect. This is a comma splice: two sentences are joined with a comma; they should be separated with a full stop or joined with a connective.
B Correct. The two sentences are separated with a full stop.
C Correct. The two sentences are joined with a connective.
5 There are eight mistakes in total in the original, including the unnecessary exclamation marks at the end of the title:
A Change of Heart[1]
I braced myself for a confrontation.**[2]** *She was looking at me like she knew I had something to say and she didn't want to hear it. My heart began to race and a strange throbbing pain pulsed in my forehead. How could I say it*?**[3]** *How could I tell her what I was thinking without upsetting her*?**[4]**
She knew something was coming.**[5]** *Tears were welling up in her dark brown eyes and her bottom lip was starting to quiver. I didn't feel much better than she did*.**[6]** *My stomach was churning and I could feel my legs shaking. I tried to speak*.**[7]** *My mouth felt like sandpaper*.**[8]** *It was dry and rough and I couldn't form the words.*

83. Commas

1/2 **A** Incorrect: They can comfort us in a crisis, help out when we're in trouble**, [comma needed here]** make us laugh or make us cry.
B Correct.
C Correct.
D Correct.
E Correct.
F Incorrect: *Although I had known her since primary school*, **[comma needed here]** *we never spoke again.*
G Incorrect: *The problem*, **[comma needed here]** *which we may not want to face, is that friends can sometimes let us down.*
H Incorrect: *A friend*, **[comma needed here]** *who I will not name*, **[comma needed here]** *once told me all my worst faults.*
I Correct.

84. Apostrophes and speech punctuation

1/2 **A** Incorrect: should be *don't.*
B Correct.
C Incorrect: should be *wouldn't.*
D Incorrect: should be *teacher's* because it is singular (one teacher).
E Incorrect: should be school's because it is possessive, not plural.
F Correct (plural: several boys' faces).
G Correct.
H Correct.
I Incorrect: *'Come over here,* **[comma needed here]***' he whispered.*

85. Colons, semi-colons, dashes, brackets and ellipses

1 Here are some examples of altered punctuation.
A There is only one thing you can do to improve your grades**: [colon, followed by lower case r for revise]** revise.
B Teachers can help**: [colon, followed by lower case t for they]** they can give revision tips and answer any questions you have about the exam.
C Revision isn't easy**: [colon, followed by lower case i for it]** it takes time and willpower.
D Exams are the problem**; [semi-colon, followed by lower case r for revision]** revision is the solution.

2/3 **A** Correct.
B Correct.
C Incorrect: *My bedroom walls are covered in scribbled revision notes and key points – not a pretty sight.* (Brackets **must** be used in pairs; dashes can be used singly.)
D Correct.

86. Putting it into practice

The article should feature a range of punctuation used accurately, including colons and semi-colons.

87. Common spelling errors 1

1 **A** *their* (not *there*)
B *would have* (not *would of*); *absolutely* (not *absolutley*)
C *effect* (not *affect*); *extremely* (not *extremley*)
D Correct.
E *There are* (not *Their our*)
F *They're* (not *there*)
G *its* (not *it's*)
H *definitely have* (not *definitley of*)
I *It's* (not *Its*); are affected (not *our effected*)
J *our* (not *are*)
K *could not have been* (not *could not of been*); *their* (not *there*)
L *negatively* (not *negativley*)
M *It's* (not *Its*).

88. Common spelling errors 2

1 **A** *where* (not *were*); *whose* (not *who's*)
B *too* (not *to*)
C *passed* (not *past*)
D *off* (not *of*)
E *You're* (not *Your*)
F *Who's* (not *Whose*)
G *were* (not *where*)
H *past* (not *passed*); *were* (not *wear*)
I *to* [an extreme] (not *too*)
J Correct.
K *you're* (not *your*)
L *off* (not *of*)
M *we're* (not *were*).

89. Common spelling errors 3

1 argument
difficult
disappoint
disappear
embarrassing
possession
beginning
recommend
occasionally
definitely
separately
conscious
conscience
experience
independence
believe
weird
business
rhythm
decision
grateful

90. Proofreading

1 The corrections are in **bold**.
Scotland is the most amazing place **I've** ever visited. **E**ven though it took ten hours to drive there it was worth it the moment **I** saw **where** we were staying: **h**uge blue lochs, rolling green hills, miles and miles of pine forest; **t**hey even looked beautiful driving **past** them in a car.
On the first day, we took the dogs for a long walk through a forest. **I**t was the **quietest** place **I've** ever been. Even with my brother **there**, all you could hear was the sound of **leaves** rustling in the breeze, the birds singing and **your** heart beating.
Our hotel was great; the **S**cottish people are so **friendly**.
I would **definitely** stay there again.

There are no questions printed on this page.

There are no questions printed on this page.

There are no questions printed on this page.

There are no questions printed on this page.

Published by Pearson Education Limited, Edinburgh Gate, Harlow, Essex, CM20 2JE.

www.pearsonschoolsandfecolleges.co.uk

Edited, produced and typeset by Wearset Ltd, Boldon, Tyne and Wear
Illustrated by Wearset Ltd
Cover illustration by Miriam Sturdee

The right of David Grant to be identified as author of this work has been asserted by him in accordance with the Copyright, Designs and Patents Act 1988.

First published 2013

17 16 15 14 13
10 9 8 7 6 5 4 3 2

British Library Cataloguing in Publication Data
A catalogue record for this book is available from the British Library

ISBN 978 1 447 94068 5

Printed by L.E.G.O.

Acknowledgements
The publisher would like to thank the following for their kind permission to reproduce their photographs:

(Key: b-bottom; c-centre; l-left; r-right; t-top)

Alamy Images: Chris Rout 46cl, Friedrich Stark 44cr, MBI 42tr, Tetra Images 38cl; **engineeringuk:** 48b; **Getty Images:** ChinaFotoPress 44bl, Cultura/Liam Norris 24cr, Photographer's Choice/David Young-Wolff 40tr, Stone/Charlie Schuck 42tl; **Masterfile UK Ltd:** 38c, Monkey Business Images 38cr; **Pearson Education Ltd:** Clark Wiseman/Studio 8 42bl; **Photos.com:** Ian Jeffery 43tl, Stockbyte 43bl; **Press Association Images:** AP/Richard Vogel 6tr; **Science Photo Library Ltd:** Philippe Psaila 105tc; **SuperStock:** Cultura Limited 43tr; **Used with kind permission from Barnardo's www.barnardos.org.uk:** 48t; **Veer/Corbis:** Roman_Shyshak 42br

All other images © Pearson Education Limited

We are grateful to the following for permission to reproduce copyright material:

Images
Poster on from "Dying to take the call" THINK! road safety poster. Reproduced by permission of the Department of Transport; Poster from "Getting into engineering", www.tomorrowsengineer.org.uk. Reproduced by permission of EngineeringUK; and poster from "Think U Know" leaflet, www.thinkuknow.co.uk, copyright © CEOP.

Text
Extract from "Clean the bones of your relatives and party in their graveyards: Welcome to the Day of the Dead", *The Daily Mail*, 02/11/2012 (Rik Sharma), copyright © Daily Mail, 2012; Extract from "Bradley Wiggins: please don't ask my wife to take a picture", *The Guardian*, 02/11/2012 (Simon Hattenstone and Peter Walker), copyright © Guardian News & Media Ltd, 2012; Extract from "Just Back: The Skeleton Coast from above", *The Daily Telegraph*, 15/06/2012 (John Roome), copyright © Telegraph Media Group Limited, 2012; Extracts from "No sticks in the mud allowed! Crazy runners play dirty in messiest obstacle course in the world", *The Daily Mail*, 14/07/2012 (Tom Gardner); "We have become a nation of cry-babies!", *The Daily Mail*, 01/10/2012 (Jan Moir); and "How GM crops have increased the use of danger pesticides and created superweeds and toxin-resistant insects", *The Daily Mail*, 02/10/2012 (Sean Poulter), copyright © Daily Mail, 2012; Extract "They are as big as Alsatians and getting bigger", *The Guardian*, 07/06/2012 (Stephen Harris), copyright © Guardian News & Media Ltd, 2012; Extracts from "Coping with the first day at school", *The Daily Telegraph*, 05/09/2012 (Rachel Halliwell); and "Sir Ranulph Fiennes: it's the winning that is important", *The Daily Telegraph*, 02/10/2012 (Harry Wallop), copyright © Telegraph Media Group Limited, 2012; Extract from *Between the Lines* by Victoria Pendleton, HarperSport, 2012, pp. 9–10. Reprinted by permission of HarperCollins Publishers Ltd © 2012 Victoria Pendleton; Extracts from "Felix Baumgartner: 'I hope I can make fear cool'", *The Guardian*, 03/11/2012 (Donald McRae); and "I was crushed by a cow", *The Guardian*, 15/06/2012 (Mike Scriven), copyright © Guardian News & Media Ltd, 2012; Extract from "At a loss in the Rocky Mountains", *The Daily Telegraph*, 05/10/2012 (Linda Fawke), copyright © Telegraph Media Group Limited, 2012; Extract adapted from "Big in Belgium the British celebrities you've never heard of", *The Guardian*, 15/03/2013 (Eleanor Tucker), copyright © Guardian News & Media Ltd, 2013; Extract from "The new global addiction: smartphones", *The Daily Telegraph*, 15/06/2012 (Damian Thompson), copyright © Telegraph Media Group Limited, 2012; Extracts from "Time to let the furry friends go", *The Guardian* 29/09/2012 (29/09/2012); and "Battery-farmed puppies are a shame on our nation", *The Guardian*, 21/09/2012 (Beverley Cuddy), copyright © Guardian News & Media Ltd 2012; Extract from "A poor school report is no barrier to success", *The Daily Telegraph*, 10/01/2012 (Max Davidson), copyright © Telegraph Media Group Limited, 2012; Extract from "Just One Little Tattoo", *The Guardian*, 11/08/2012 (Tess Morgan), copyright © Guardian News & Media Ltd, 2012; Extract from "Life's a lottery but sometimes the good guys win", *The Daily Mail*, 16/08/2012 (Jan Moir), copyright © Daily Mail, 2012; Extract from *The Accidental Adventurer* by Ben Fogle, published by Bantam Press, 2012, pp. 11–12. Reprinted by permission of The Random House Group Limited and Lucas Alexander Whitley Ltd on behalf of Rambling Ruminations Ltd; Extracts from "Is your Facebook page a lie?", *The Guardian*, 08/10/2012 (Libby Page); and "I'd risk my life to rescue my dog; that's just what owners do", *The Guardian*, 28/09/2012 (Michele Hanson), copyright © Guardian News & Media Ltd 2012; Extract from "Just back: from dawn to dusk on Bondi Beach", *The Daily Telegraph*, 18/05/2012 (Janet Rogers), copyright © Telegraph Media Group Limited, 2012; Extract from "Having friends and going swimming are more important than money to today's youth", *The Daily Mail*, 07/10/2012, copyright © Daily Mail, 2012; Extract from "You are inferior, you will be exterminated!", *The Daily Telegraph*, 05/11/2012 (Johnny Morris), copyright © Telegraph Media Group Limited, 2012; Extract from "Top Footballers See Pay Rise By 1500%". Sky, 20/08/2012, http://news.sky.com. Reproduced with permission; Extracts from "The dogs who listen to children reading", *The Guardian*, 28/02/2011 (Patrick Barkham); and "Ask the experts: painting vacations and adventure sports", *The Guardian*, 17/08/2012, copyright © Guardian News & Media Ltd, 2011, 2012; Extracts from "Do you think I'm made of money?", *The Daily Mail*, 05/11/2012 (Kerry McDermot); "Father who lost arm in work accident has bionic 'Terminator hand'", *The Daily Mail*, 05/11/2012 (Anna Hodgekiss); and "Real Lives: Teenage Cancer", *The Daily Mail*, 04/11/2012 (Joanna Moorhead), copyright © Daily Mail 2012.

Every effort has been made to contact copyright holders of material reproduced in this book. Any omissions will be rectified in subsequent printings if notice is given to the publishers.

In the writing of this book, no AQA examiners authored sections relevant to examination papers for which they have responsibility.